gateway scien

CW00850764

revision guide

OCR Science for GCSE

Separate

Biology

Elaine Gill

Series editor: Bob McDuell

Heinemann

Heinemann is an imprint of Pearson Education Limited, a company incorporated in England and Wales, having its registered office at Edinburgh Gate, Harlow, Essex, CM20 2JE. Registered company number: 872828

Heinemann is a registered trademark of Pearson Education Limited

© Harcourt Education Limited 2007

First published 2007

11
10 9 8 7 6

British Library Cataloguing in Publication Data is available from the British Library on request.

ISBN: 978 0 435675 48 6

Designed by Wooden Ark
Project managed, edited and typeset by Bookcraft Ltd (Alex Sharpe, Project Manager)

Pearson project team: David Cooke, Andrew Halcro-Johnston, Ross Laman, Sarah Ross, Ruth Simms, Iti Singh, Peter Stratton

Original illustrations © Harcourt Education Limited 2007

Illustrated by Bookcraft India Pvt Ltd (Gemma Raj), HL Studios

Printed and bound in China (CTPS/06)

Cover photo © Getty Images

Every effort has been made to contact copyright holders of material reproduced in this book. Any omissions will be rectified in subsequent printings if notice is given to the publishers.

About this book

This OCR Gateway Biology revision guide will help you revise for the OCR Gateway Biology exams. One exam consists of modules B1, B2 and B3 and the other of B4, B5 and B6. The guide summarises what you have learnt and links directly to the OCR Biology specification for Higher tier.

This guide is broken down into the six biology modules: B1, B2, B3, B4, B5 and B6. Each module covers eight items (a–h), for example B1a–B1h. You will find some items are combined into one section, for example B1a & B1b.

Each section starts with a **learning outcome** which summarises the main points covered. This will help you to focus on what you need to revise in that section.

Key words are shown in bold and you will find them indexed at the back of the guide. **Equations** are highlighted to help you use and apply them.

The exam may ask you to consider ideas about 'How science works'. The **How science works** boxes will help you apply this thinking to your answers. Remember that you should be continually questioning how scientists collect data, use and interpret evidence.

Exam tips highlight common mistakes and give you advice about exam preparation so you can achieve better grades.

You will find lots of simple, full colour diagrams, including **spider diagrams**, to help with your revision and to make the content more digestible. Try drawing your own spider diagrams to help you remember key concepts.

We have given you **'Test yourself' questions** at the end of each section to help you to check that you have understood the content. Use the **answers** at the back of the guide to check whether you have got them all correct – if not, go back and revise that section again.

The revision guide is based on the new specification and the example **exam-style questions** on page 75 will give you valuable preparation for the exams.

Remember that these questions are for revision and homework. The exams will also contain some recall and one-mark questions. In your revision you should think beyond the basic ideas so that you have a better understanding for the exams.

The **answers** that follow the questions will allow you to check your progress and improve next time.

Good luck with your exams!

Contents

B1a Fit for life &
B1b What's for lunch?

After revising these items you should:

- be able to explain blood pressure, respiration, fitness and diet.

Heart and blood pressure

Exercise increases blood pressure. If you have your blood pressure taken when you visit the doctor or hospital, you are given two numbers.

- The first number is the **systolic** pressure.
- The second usually a lower number, is the **diastolic** pressure.

Blood pressure is measured in millimetres of mercury (mm Hg).

The table shows normal, high and low blood pressures.

Blood pressure	Systolic (mm Hg)	Diastolic (mm Hg)
normal	130	75
high	160	105
low	90	40

High blood pressure can cause:

- weak blood vessels to burst
- strokes
- kidney damage
- damage to the brain.

Low blood pressure can cause:

- poor circulation
- dizziness
- fainting.

Blood pressure varies with age and lifestyle:

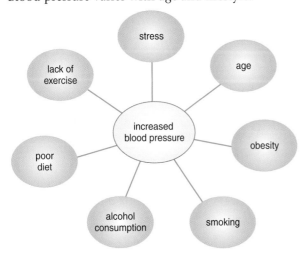

How science works

We can collect data about the blood pressure and lifestyle of many people. This data is analysed and conclusions drawn.

As a result, suggestions can be made to those with high or low blood pressure on how to change their lifestyle to try to keep their blood pressure within normal ranges.

For example, those who are obese with high blood pressure could be advised to lose weight. This should bring their blood pressure down.

Fitness

The time it takes for your pulse rate to get back to normal is one way of measuring fitness. Fitness is the ability of your body to carry out physical exercise. This is not the same as being healthy or disease free. Fitness can also be assessed by measuring:

- stamina
- agility
- flexibility
- speed
- strength
- cardiovascular efficiency.

How science works

You can measure a person's fitness in several different ways. You can measure strength by seeing how many press ups they can do. You can measure recovery rate by calculating how long it takes for their pulse rate to return to normal. The data can be evaluated and its validity and reliability assessed.

Respiration

Every cell in your body respires all the time. This releases energy from **glucose**, which enables you to carry out all your daily activities. There are two types of **respiration**:

- Aerobic – using oxygen.
- Anaerobic – without oxygen.

The word and symbol equations for **aerobic respiration** are:

$$\text{glucose} + \text{oxygen} \rightarrow \textbf{carbon dioxide} + \text{water} + \text{energy}$$

$$C_6H_{12}O_6 + 6O_2 \rightarrow 6CO_2 + 6H_2O + \text{energy}$$

The word equation for **anaerobic respiration** is:

glucose $\longrightarrow$ **lactic acid** + energy

Anaerobic respiration is carried out when the body cannot provide enough oxygen to the cells. This type of respiration does not break down the glucose completely. It produces lactic acid which accumulates in the muscles and causes pain (cramp) and fatigue.

Anaerobic respiration takes place during hard exercise.

- The muscles need more oxygen and glucose to release the energy needed.
- Anaerobic respiration causes an **oxygen debt**, which has to be repaid.
- Therefore extra oxygen is needed when exercise has finished to break down the lactic acid.
- Continued panting replaces oxygen, allowing aerobic respiration.
- The heart beats faster to try to circulate more blood to the muscles.
- The blood also carries lactic acid to the liver where it is broken down.

Anaerobic respiration releases much less energy than aerobic respiration.

If you are running to train for an important sporting event, your pulse rate and breathing rate increase. When you stop, your pulse and breathing rates return to normal. The length of time it takes to return to normal depends on your fitness. A professional athlete's pulse rate returns to normal more quickly than an unfit person's.

Balanced diet

A balanced diet means eating the correct nutrients in the correct quantities. The diet for each person depends on their age, gender and activity.

- If they are doing a manual job they will need more of some nutrients.
- Vegetarians and vegans need a different diet from those who eat meat so that they get all their essential amino acids.
- People with allergies need to avoid certain foods. If you are allergic to peanuts or have a reaction to gluten, then you must avoid food containing these items.
- Some people cannot eat certain foods for religious reasons.

First class **proteins** (from animal protein) contain all the essential amino acids we need. Plant protein only contains some of the amino acids we need. Diets lacking in protein lead to the deficiency disease **kwashiorkor**. This is common in developing countries.

The amount of protein we need each day is called the recommended daily average (RDA) and can be calculated.

RDA (in grams) = body mass (in kilograms) × 0.75

Body mass index

The BMI (body mass index) is used to find out whether people are the right weight or not. Calculate it by measuring your mass in kilograms and your height in metres and use this formula:

$$BMI = \frac{\text{mass in kilograms}}{(\text{height in metres})^2}$$

By using BMI charts, this index tells us whether we are underweight, healthy, overweight or obese.

BMI	State of weight
up to 19	underweight
19–24	healthy weight
25–28	overweight
over 28	obese

Obesity in young people is a major cause for concern. It can lead to many long-term illnesses. The desire for a 'perfect' body can lead to low self-esteem and poor self-image. This can lead to a poor diet.

Digestion

Food is made of large, **insoluble** pieces. It must be broken down into small, soluble molecules.
This is done:

- physically – in the mouth by the teeth and in the stomach by squeezing the food
- chemically – in the digestive system with the help of **enzymes**.

The table shows three food groups, the enzymes that help to break them down, where the enzyme is made and what the food is broken down into.

Food group	Enzymes	Where the enzyme is made	Product
protein	protease	stomach small intestine pancreas	amino acids
fat	lipase	pancreas	fatty acids glycerol
carbohydrate	amylase	mouth small intestine	simple sugars

Digestion takes place in our digestive system. Different parts of the digestive system are specialised for different functions.

- Hydrochloric acid is added in the stomach to kill bacteria and to provide the correct pH for the **protease** enzymes.
- **Bile** is added in the small intestine to **emulsify** fats. This improves fat digestion by breaking the fat into smaller pieces. This increases the surface area for enzyme action.
- The small molecules are absorbed into the blood plasma or the lymph. This happens in the small intestine by **diffusion**.

Exam tip

You should know the parts of the digestive system and the function of each part.

Work out a mnemonic to help you remember the parts.

Test yourself

1 What changes could someone with high blood pressure make to their lifestyle to bring their blood pressure back to normal?

2 What is the difference in energy output of the two types of respiration?

3 Why does low blood pressure cause fainting?

4 Why do active people need more food than inactive ones?

5 How does the emulsification of fats help digestion?

6 Calculate the BMI of a person who is 1.8 m tall and weighs 80 kg. Which category do they come in: underweight, healthy, overweight or obese?

7 Calculate the RDA for protein for a child who weighs 20 kg and a teenager who weighs 45 kg. Why is there a difference?

B1c Keeping healthy

After revising these items you should:

- understand what makes us ill and what makes us better.

Causes of disease

The diagram shows the causes of disease.

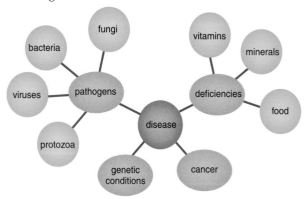

Cancer occurs when cells divide in an uncontrolled way producing a mass called a **tumour**. There are two types of tumour:

- **Benign** – tumours that stop growing.
- **Malignant** – tumours that continue to grow and spread, which makes them dangerous.

We can make changes to our lifestyle to reduce the risk of getting some cancers.

The table shows some of many causes of disease.

Disease	Cause of disease
scurvy	vitamin deficiency
anaemia	mineral deficiency
diabetes	body disorder
red–green **colour blindness**	genetic

Malaria

Facts about malaria:

- Malaria is caused by a **parasite**.
- A parasite is an **organism** that lives on or in another living organism causing it harm.
- The malarial parasite lives in the human blood and liver.
- The parasite is spread by the mosquito.
- The human and the mosquito are **hosts** to the parasite.
- An organism that carries parasites from one organism to another is called a **vector**.

Controlling vectors

Malaria can be prevented by destroying the vectors. This knowledge is expanded in the table.

Method	How this stops the vector spreading disease
open water can be drained	there is nowhere for mosquitoes to lay their eggs
open water can be sprayed with chemicals	kills the mosquito eggs, larvae and pupae
fish can be introduced into ponds	fish eat the mosquito larvae
nets can be placed over beds	stops mosquito biting human
humans can take **drugs**	kills the stage of the mosquito in the human

Antibodies and antigens

Pathogens are microorganisms that cause disease. These microorganisms damage cells in our bodies, or produce **toxins**. Each microorganism has a specific **antigen** on its surface. Our bodies produce specific **antibodies** to each antigen. The antibody attaches itself to the antigen and kills the pathogen.

The diagram shows how antibodies attack antigens.

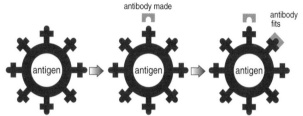

Immunity

There are two types of immunity:

- In **active immunity** we make our own antibodies, copies of which remain in our bodies to be used when another infection occurs.
- In **passive immunity** we have an injection of antibodies made by someone else. This type of immunity does not last long.

Process of immunisation

Immunisation can be done artificially by having an injection of a weakened form of the pathogen (vaccine), which our bodies make antibodies against. If we are ever infected by the live pathogen our bodies are ready to destroy it.

New vaccines continually need to be produced as pathogens keep changing and the antibodies will not work.

Bacterial and fungal infections can be treated by taking **antibiotics**. Over-prescribing and the wrong use of antibiotics have resulted in resistant forms of bacteria evolving. Antibiotics need to be used carefully to prevent the increase of resistant strains of bacteria developing, e.g. MRSA.

The table shows some benefits and risks of immunisation.

Benefits	Risks
we avoid catching diseases	some people have reactions to the vaccines
long-term protection	the weakened viral particles can be passed through the digestive system if taken orally. They pass out in the faeces and could then infect somebody else
eradication of some diseases	

Drug testing

New drugs have to be tested before they can be used to treat humans. This is to ensure they are safe to use. They are tested in several ways.

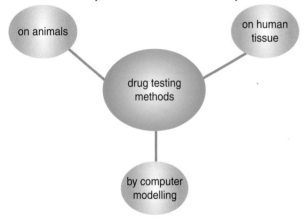

After testing has taken place, the effectiveness of the drugs is assessed by doing blind and double-blind drug trials. Placebos are also used.

Blind trials are when a patient does not know whether they are taking the real drug or a fake. The fake is called a placebo. A double-blind trial is when the doctor also does not know which one the patient is taking.

Test yourself

1 Look at the pie chart about deaths from cancer in 2004.

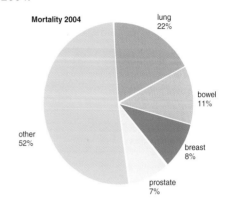

   (a) What percentage of the deaths was from lung cancer?
   (b) Which cancer was responsible for 8% of deaths?
   (c) Which of the cancers named is only found in men?
   (d) Suggest other types of cancer.

2 How do the procedures used to prevent malaria work?

3 Why is passive immunity short-lived?

4 What are the objections to the forms of drug testing shown in the diagram opposite?

5 How can you change your lifestyle to reduce the risk of developing cancers?

B1d Keeping in touch

After revising this item you should:

● understand how our bodies communicate.

The eye

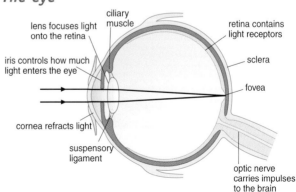

The table shows the functions of parts of the eye.

Part	Function
cornea	refracts light
iris	controls how much light enters the pupil
lens	focuses light onto the retina
retina	contains light **receptors**
optic nerve	carries impulses to the brain

The position of the two eyes on the head is important. It means you have monocular or binocular vision.

- Monocular vision – the two eyes are on the side of your head. This means you can see all round but you cannot judge distances. This is important for animals that are hunted (**prey** so that they can see **predators**).
- **Binocular vision** – the eyes are on the front of your head. This means you can judge distances but you cannot see all round (without moving your head).

How we see

Light enters the eye from the object. Light is refracted by the cornea and then focused by the lens onto the retina. The ciliary muscles and the suspensory ligament cause the lens to change shape, which allows focusing. This is called accommodation and happens every time we look at objects at different distances from the eye.

Here are some other things you need to know about the eye and vision.

- We have binocular vision. This enables us to judge distances accurately.
- Accommodation does not take place as effectively in older people, so they need reading glasses.
- Colour vision is possible because the retina contains three types of cones which detect red, green and blue light.
- Colour blindness is an inherited condition which means you cannot see colours correctly.

- **Short sight** is caused by the light rays focusing too soon, in front of the retina, because the eyeball is the wrong shape. We can correct this using concave lenses or cornea surgery.

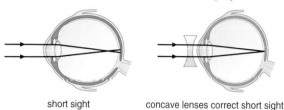

short sight   concave lenses correct short sight

- **Long sight** is caused by the light rays focusing behind the retina. We can correct this using convex lenses.

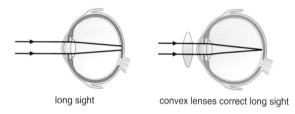

long sight   convex lenses correct long sight

The table shows the causes of eye defects.

Eye defect	Cause of defect
red–green colour blindness	this is inherited from parents and is a lack of specialised cells in the retina
short sight	eyeball or lens is the wrong shape
long sight	eyeball or lens is the wrong shape

The nervous system

The nervous system is made up of individual cells called **neurones**. Neurones are the longest cells in the body – they can be over one metre in length. Nerve impulses are carried in the **axon** of a neurone.

The **sensory** neurones carry information in the form of electrical impulses from the five senses to the central nervous system (CNS). The **motor** neurones carry information from the CNS to the muscles.

Neurones are adapted to their function by:

- length – the impulses can travel to all parts of the body
- having an insulating **sheath** – this keeps the impulse on the right track. It cannot get lost
- having branched endings (**dendrites**) – one neurone can communicate with many others.

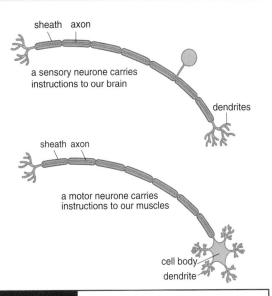

sheath axon

a sensory neurone carries
instructions to our brain

dendrites

sheath axon

a motor neurone carries
instructions to our muscles

cell body
dendrite

Exam tip

*You should be able to draw and label a sensory and
a motor neurone.*

The junction of two neurones is called a **synapse**.

Facts about synapses:

- The neurones meet at synapses.
- Synapses are tiny gaps.
- The information is passed across the gap
  by diffusion of chemicals called neuro-
  transmitters.
- The chemical binds with receptor molecules on
  the membrane of the next neurone.
- This causes a new impulse to be formed.

Reflex arc

The diagram shows a **reflex arc**.

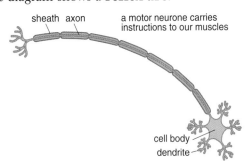

sheath axon   a motor neurone carries
                    instructions to our muscles

cell body
dendrite

In a reflex arc, there is a set response to a specific
stimulus. It always follows this pattern. The table
shows this pattern and parts of a spinal reflex
pathway.

Pattern	Example
stimulus	pin sticking into your finger
receptor	pain receptor in your skin
sensory neurone	sensory neurone in your arm
CNS	spinal cord
motor neurone	motor neurone in your arm
effector	muscle
response	pull arm away from pin

Test yourself

1 How does binocular vision help predators?

2 How do the ciliary muscles and the suspensory
   ligament change the shape of the lens?

3 How are neurones adapted for their function of
   transmitting impulses?

4 By which process does the neuro-transmitter pass
   across the synapse?

B1e Drugs and you

After revising this item you should:

- understand about drugs, including alcohol
  and tobacco, and their effects on the body.

Drugs

Drugs are chemicals that produce changes within
the body. The table shows the different types of
drugs and the effects that they have.

Type of drug	Effect	Example
depressants	slows the brain down	temazepam, alcohol, solvents
stimulants	increases brain activity	nicotine, ecstasy, caffeine
painkillers	reduces pain	aspirin, heroin
performance enhancers	improves athletic performance	anabolic steroids
hallucinogens	changes what we see and hear	LSD, cannabis

Depressants and **stimulants** act on the synapses
of the nervous system.

- Depressants slow down transmission across
  synapses.
- Stimulants speed up transmission across synapses.

Drugs can belong to one or more of these categories:

- legal
- illegal
- social

Legal classification of drugs

The table shows examples of the three classes of drugs.

Class	Example	Other information
A	heroine, cocaine, ecstasy, LSD	possession can lead to seven years in prison
B	amphetamines, barbiturates	possession can lead to five years in prison
C	prescribed drugs, cannabis	possession carries lightest penalties

This classification has consequences both at school, local and national levels. The table shows these arguments.

Arguments for:
People should be free to choose whether they take drugs or not.
Police spend too much time catching drug users.
Legalised drugs would be cheaper and safer for the users.
Cheaper drugs would mean less crime as users try to fund their habit.
Healthworkers would know who the users were and be able to help them kick the habit.
Free hypodermic needles would reduce the risk of drug users reusing them and passing on dangerous diseases such as AIDS.

Arguments against:
Increased drug use may lead to an increase in crime to pay for drugs.
People need to be protected against themselves.
Softer drugs such as cannabis may lead to using harder drugs such as heroin.
Drug use would increase if drugs were legalised.
Drugs affect reaction times. Road accidents and other types of accident would increase.
Cannabis abuse can lead to an increased risk of developing mental illnesses such as psychosis and schizophrenia.

Exam tip

You should know the arguments for and against the legal classification of drugs.

How science works

Decisions made about the classification of drugs affect everybody. Some people think that drugs should be legalised. Others think the opposite. Some people claim that cannabis has some medical uses and want it to be freely available.

Smoking

The table shows some of the substances in cigarettes and cigarette smoke and the effects they have.

Substance	Effects
the drug **nicotine**	nicotine is addictive
tar	tar is an irritant and can cause cancer
tiny particles	these accumulate in the lungs and can lead to bronchitis and emphysema
carbon monoxide	it combines irreversibly with haemoglobin in red blood cells. This prevents oxygen being carried by the red blood cells and may lead to heart disease
other chemicals	these stop the **cilia** from working

The trachea, bronchi and bronchioles are lined with mucus to trap particles and microbes, and cilia which waft the mucus upwards to the back of the throat where it is swallowed. In a smoker, the mucus cannot be removed and builds up.

People cough to try to get rid of this mucus. The mucus can become infected; this is the cause of bronchitis. Sometimes the air sacs are damaged and break down, leading to holes in the lung tissue. This is called emphysema.

Alcohol

Alcohol is a poisonous drug. It is removed from the body by the liver. Drinking too much alcohol over a long period of time can cause damage to the liver (**cirrhosis**), brain and nervous system.

Alcohol consumption is measured in units. The table shows how many units different drinks contain.

Drink	Units
one pint of beer	2
one small glass of wine	1
one measure of spirit, e.g. whisky	1
one small glass of sherry/port	1

This is only a guide as alcoholic drinks have different alcohol contents. The recommended maximum weekly amount is:

- 14 units for women
- 21 units for men.

Alcohol also slows our reaction times. It increases the chance of having an accident whilst driving or operating machinery.

Alcohol level in blood (mg/litre)	Reaction time compared with normal
0.8 the legal limit (two pints of beer)	4x slower
1.2 (3 pints of beer)	15x slower
1.6 (4 pints of beer)	30x slower

How science works

Alcoholic drinks such as wine now have a higher alcohol content than they did 10 years ago. What problem can this cause the drinker and what can governments do?

Some responses could be to give more information about alcohol content, regulations on strength of wines, more breath testing and so on.

Test yourself

1   Name two socially acceptable drugs, two illegal drugs and two legal drugs.

2   What happens to the birth weight of babies born to mothers who smoke during pregnancy?

3   Look at the diagrams of glasses of alcoholic drink.

beer 1 pint — 2 units
beer ½ pint — 1 units
wine — 1 unit
spirit — 1 unit

   (a)   Anne drinks two glasses of wine and a double gin. How many units of alcohol has she had to drink?
   (b)   How many pints of beer does Sanjay drink if he has drunk six units?
   (c)   How many units are there in a cocktail containing two spirits and one wine?

4   Why is there a legal limit for the level of alcohol in the blood of drivers?

B1f Staying in balance

After revising this item you should:

- understand how our bodies control their internal environment.

Homeostasis

Homeostasis is the maintenance of a constant internal environment. It involves balancing daily inputs and outputs. It involves negative feedback mechanisms. This is so that cells can function properly. Homeostatic mechanisms enable humans to live in almost every environment on the Earth.

The diagram shows the effect of negative feedback.

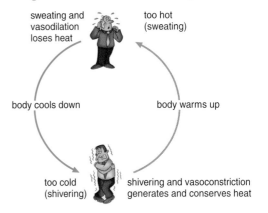

sweating and vasodilation loses heat
too hot (sweating)
body cools down
body warms up
too cold (shivering)
shivering and vasoconstriction generates and conserves heat

When we are hot, our brain detects the temperature of the blood passing through. It sends impulses to the skin so that the capillaries dilate. More blood flows to the skin and we lose heat and cool down. The brain then senses the blood is cooler and impulses are sent to the skin to constrict the capillaries and so less blood flows to the skin. This means less heat is lost. It is a constant monitoring system.

Exam tip

You should know what a negative feedback mechanism is and how it works in homeostasis.

What does the body try to keep constant?

- blood glucose levels
- body temperature at 37°C
- water content   •   carbon dioxide levels.

Controlling body temperature

The skin controls body temperature. The diagram shows a cross-section of the skin and the parts involved in temperature regulation.

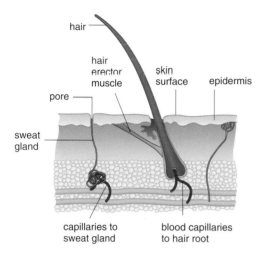

The body temperature should be maintained at 37°C so that enzymes can work properly. Enzymes are damaged if the temperature is too high and are ineffective if the temperature is too low.

We keep warm by:

- **vasoconstriction** – the blood capillaries in the skin constrict, therefore less blood flows through them so less heat can be lost through the skin
- shivering – the muscles contract, releasing heat which warms us up.

We keep cool by:

- **vasodilation** – the blood capillaries in the skin widen, therefore more blood flows through them so more heat can be lost through the skin
- sweating – sweat is produced on the surface of the skin. Heat from the body is used to evaporate this sweat therefore the body loses its heat to the environment and cools down.

Exam tip

You should know the detail of how the mechanisms for keeping warm and cool work.

Don't forget that it is the evaporation that is important in sweating.

How science works

Sometimes the body cannot control its temperature. If the body temperature rises too much, then we suffer from **heat-stroke**. This can lead to **dehydration** and death. If the body temperature falls too low, we suffer from **hypothermia**. This can also lead to death.

The body temperature is monitored by the brain. If this centre detects that the temperature is too high or too low, it initiates the mechanisms that return the temperature to normal.

Sex hormones

Sex hormones are responsible for the secondary sexual characteristics that develop at puberty. The table shows the changes that happen to males and females.

Change	Male	Female
voice breaks	✓	x
hair grows on face and body	✓	x
hair grows under the arms	✓	✓
pubic hair grows	✓	✓
more muscular	✓	x
genitals develop	✓	✓
sperm production starts	✓	x
breasts develop	x	✓
hips widen	x	✓
periods start	x	✓

The female hormones are **oestrogen** and **progesterone**. These hormones control the menstrual cycle.

- Oestrogen causes the lining of the uterus to thicken and re-grow blood vessels.
- Progesterone maintains the lining of the uterus. A fall in progesterone levels triggers menstruation.

Ovulation is controlled by these hormones together with other hormones produced by the pituitary gland in the brain. We can control **fertility** by using artificial sex hormones (**contraceptive** pill and fertility drugs).

The contraceptive pill lowers fertility. The contraceptive pill mimics female hormones to prevent the body from ovulating. If there are no eggs there can be no fertilisation and no babies. Some drugs, e.g. fertility drugs, promote ovulation and cause more eggs to be released so that there is more chance of fertilisation. Sometimes women donate eggs to infertile women.

Diabetes

Diabetes is caused when the body does not produce enough **insulin**. Insulin converts excess sugar in the blood into glycogen, which is stored in the liver. Diabetes can be controlled by being careful what you eat – avoiding too much sweet food. Some people need to inject themselves with insulin to control their diabetes. The dose of insulin will depend on their diet and how active they are.

Test yourself

1. How are humans adapted to keep warm?
2. Explain the function of oestrogen and progesterone.
3. How does the contraceptive pill prevent pregnancy and how do fertility drugs help a woman to get pregnant?
4. How can a person with diabetes control it?

B1g Gene control & B1h Who am I?

After revising these items you should:

- understand the structure of DNA, chromosomes and genes and how DNA enables us to inherit features from our parents.

DNA, chromosomes and genes

All human body cells except sex cells (**gametes**) have the same number of **chromosomes**. Cells have 46 chromosomes which make up 23 pairs. Different species have different overall numbers of chromosomes.

Chromosomes carry information in the form of **genes**. Chromosomes are long coiled molecules of **DNA** divided into regions called genes. Each gene contains a different sequence of **bases** and this

coded information is called the **genetic code**. The genetic code controls cell activity and some of the characteristics of the organism. All genes are in every cell but only some of them are 'switched on'. Different sets of genes are switched on in different cells, so they all perform their specific function.

Genes are made of a chemical called DNA. Here are some facts about DNA.

- It is the code that makes a human being.
- It can copy itself exactly so the code can be passed on to the next generation.
- It is coiled into a double helix so that it is very small.
- It is so small that it can be stored in the nucleus of every cell.
- It controls how cells function by controlling protein production.
- It is made of chemicals called bases.
- There are four bases whose names are represented by A, T, C and G.

Sexual reproduction

Gametes contain 23 chromosomes, half the number in a body cell.

When gametes join together during fertilisation, the full number of chromosomes is restored to 46. A baby inherits half its DNA from its mother and half from its father, making it a unique individual. Identical twins have exactly the same DNA. Everyone else has different DNA and this leads to variation.

Variation occurs because we inherit different combinations of genes from our parents. Variation is also caused by random fertilisation. Any sperm can fertilise any egg, and both contain different combinations of genes.

How science works

International cooperation has allowed scientists to map every gene in the nucleus of a human cell. This is the Human Genome Project.

This is a massive job which has only been achieved by scientists working together. This is unusual as scientists often work individually or in small groups, and are often competing with each other to make a discovery.

Mutations

DNA can be easily damaged. These changes are called **mutations**. A mutation is a:

- change in the sequence of bases
- removal of one or more bases
- addition of one or more bases.

As a result of a mutation the protein that the gene codes for is changed.

Mutations can be beneficial or harmful. Most are harmful. Mutations can be caused by radiation or chemicals or they can occur spontaneously.

If a mutation occurs in the production of a gamete, the mutation can be passed on to the next generation. These gene mutations are usually recessive and are masked by the correct gene from the other parent. Occasionally a baby gets a faulty gene from both parents, and then the baby will not be healthy. This is why a child may have cystic fibrosis. A child who has one faulty gene should be healthy.

Boy or girl?

Inheritance of sex is controlled by whole chromosomes not individual genes. Humans have two sex chromosomes, X and Y. Males have one X chromosome and one Y chromosome whereas females have two X chromosomes. The punnet square shows how sex is inherited.

		mum	
		X	X
dad	X	XX	XX
	Y	XY	XY

Alleles

Cells in a baby contain two complete sets of instructions, one from the mother and one from the father. This means there are two versions of every gene, called **alleles**. The baby only uses one of each pair of alleles.

The table shows the meanings of some terms used in genetics.

Term	Meaning
dominant allele	these alleles are the code that is used
recessive allele	these alleles are the code that is not used
homozygous	two alleles are the same
heterozygous	two alleles are different

The dominant allele is always represented by a capital letter. The recessive allele is represented by the same letter in lower case.

Breeding experiments

Mendel carried out experiments using pea plants. He crossed a homozygous tall plant with a homozygous short plant and found that all the offspring were tall. This type of cross using one characteristic is a monohybrid cross. It can be shown in two ways.

		tall	
		T	T
short	t	Tt	Tt
	t	Tt	Tt

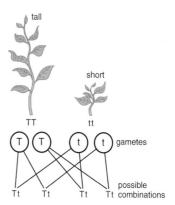

It is possible for two tall pea plants to produce short plants. The punnet square below shows the genetic diagram.

		tall	
		T	t
tall	T	TT	Tt
	t	Tt	tt

Exam tip

You should be able to construct a punnet square to predict the probabilities of inherited disorders passing to the next generation.

Genes or environment?

Scientists are trying to determine the relative importance of our genes versus the environment in making us who we are. It is a combination of both, but we don't know how much each one contributes.

There is a big debate about this in relation to intelligence, sporting ability and health.

Do you really want to know?

The table shows the benefits and disadvantages of knowing whether we have a genetic disorder that can be passed on to our children.

Benefits	Disadvantages
Knowing about our genes can enable us to decide whether or not to have children. If we knew that both our partner and ourselves were carriers for the cystic fibrosis gene, we would know that there was a one in four risk of having a child with cystic fibrosis. We would then decide whether or not to have children or take some other course of action, such as having the gametes checked, to see if they were normal.	Society has not yet decided who owns the right to know about our personal DNA.
If we knew we had a high risk of dying from heart disease we could be more careful about our lifestyle and the food that we ate.	Some insurance companies are asking clients if they have ever had any DNA tests. If they find that the person is at risk they may refuse to insure that person or raise their premiums. This will enable them to make more money for their shareholders and keep premiums down for their other clients. This means that some people may be put off having tests to find out if they are at risk from genetic disease.

Test yourself

1 Name the gametes in a human.

2 Explain how gender is inherited.

3 What does heterozygous mean?

4 In Mendel's experiments with pea plants, he crossed two tall plants together and obtained plants with these genotypes.

    Complete the table to show which plants will be tall and which will be short. What is the ratio of tall to short plants?

Genotype	Tall or short?
TT	
Tt	
tT	
tt	

5 Huntington's disease is a genetic disorder that affects one in 20 000 people.

    Huntington's disease is caused by a dominant faulty allele (H).

    The diagram shows a family tree.

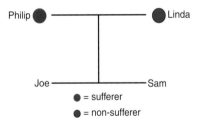

    (a) What are the genotypes of Philip and Linda?
    (b) What is the probability of both Joe and Sam inheriting the condition?

B2a Ecology in our school grounds & B2b Grouping organisms

Counting and identifying organisms

It is difficult to count all the organisms in an **ecosystem**. Instead scientists sample the **populations** of organisms in order to get an estimate of the total number of individuals. A population is a breeding group of animals or plants in the ecosystem and there are many ways of sampling it, for example:

- quadrats
- pooters
- pit-fall traps
- nets
- capture and release.

Limitations of counting and collecting methods:

- Sample size will affect accuracy of estimate.
- Samples may be unrepresentative of the population.

Exam tip

You should know how to use each of the sampling methods and remember that the sample must be large enough to be representative.

When studying an ecosystem, it is important to be able to identify the organisms that live in it. This can be done by using a **key**. Keys divide organisms into smaller and smaller groups.

Ecosystems

An ecosystem is a place or **habitat** together with all the organisms that live there. Examples of natural ecosystems are:

- rainforest
- river
- meadow
- desert

These ecosystems have many different **species** living in them. They have a high **biodiversity**.

Other ecosystems are created by humans. These are artificial and usually have a lower biodiversity.

One example is a field of wheat. The farmer has to use pesticides to stop other species growing and fertilisers to make the wheat grow well.

Some ecosystems are still unexplored and may contain undiscovered species.

Classification

All livings organisms are different and can be put into groups. This is called classification. Organisms can be classified into animals and plants.

Characteristics that place an organism into the animal kingdom
They can move independently.
They do not have chloroplasts.
They cannot make their own food.
They are more compact (this helps with movement).

Characteristics that place an organism into the plant kingdom
They cannot move independently.
They contain chloroplasts, which makes them green.
They can make their own food.
They spread out more (because they cannot move).

Some organisms cannot be placed into one of these two groups, because they have characteristics which place them in both or neither group; for example Fungi and *Euglena*.

Animals can be divided into two groups:

- **Vertebrates** – animals with backbones.
- **Invertebrates** – animals without backbones.

The table shows the five vertebrate groups, an example of each and the characteristics of the group.

Group	Example	Characteristics
fish	salmon	wet scales gills
amphibian	frog	moist permeable skin
reptile	crocodile	dry scales
bird	blackbird	feathers beak
mammal	human	fur produces milk

Archaeopteryx is an example of an organism that is difficult to classify. It does not fit into one of the vertebrate groups because it has both reptilian and bird features.

Species

Organisms are further divided until there is only one type of organism in the group. This group is a species. Every species has two names. This way of naming species is called the **binomial** system.

How science works

Scientists realised that there were many different types of organisms in the world. They collected information about these organisms and tried to put them into groups. This helped to develop the way organisms are classified.

Now when a new organism is found, it is placed into a kingdom and eventually needs a binomial name.

The first name is the same as similar animals but the second name is often based on the person who discovered it.

Organisms that belong to the same species are capable of interbreeding to produce fertile offspring.

Occasionally members of different species can reproduce. Their offspring are **hybrids**. Animal hybrids are infertile and cannot reproduce. It is difficult to classify hybrids.

Species that are similar tend to live in similar types of habitats. If they live in different habitats then they may have different features because they need different features to survive. Although their features are different, they may have evolved from a common ancestor. The diagram shows the ancestry of humans and apes.

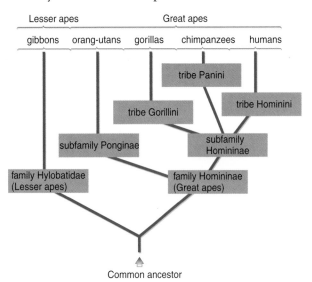

Common ancestor

Exam tip

You do not need to learn this diagram for the exam but you could be given the information and asked to use it.

Different species that live in the same habitat have evolved similar features so that they can survive in that habitat. Dolphins and whales are mammals but appear similar to sharks, which are fish. This is because these organisms all have to be able to swim in water, so they are streamlined and have fins.

Similarities and differences between species can be explained by **evolution** and ecological relationships.

Test yourself

1 Give two examples of unexplored ecosystems.

2 In a 0.5 square metre quadrat 20 dandelion plants are counted. Estimate how many dandelions there are in a 100 square metre field. Why might this answer be inaccurate? Explain how you could get a better estimate of the number of dandelion plants in this field.

3 The diagram shows five organisms.

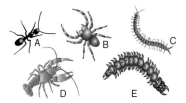

Use this key to identify them.

		Yes	No
1	Does it have more than 10 legs?	go to 2	go to 3
2	Does it have two pairs of legs per segment?	millipede	centipede
3	Does it have three parts to its body?	insect	go to 4
4	Does it have eight legs?	arachnid	crustacean

4 Name a group of organisms which have neither animal nor plant characteristics.

5 Name an organism which has both animal and plant characteristics.

6 What is the binomial name of a human?

7 Mules are hybrids. How are they produced?

B2c The food factory

After revising this item you should:

- understand how plants make food by photosynthesis, how the rate of photosynthesis can be increased and how plants use the food they make.

Photosynthesis

Plants make their own food by a process called photosynthesis.

$$\text{carbon dioxide} + \text{water} \xrightarrow[\text{chlorophyll}]{\text{light energy}} \text{glucose} + \text{oxygen}$$

$$6CO_2 + 6H_2O \xrightarrow[\text{chlorophyll}]{\text{light energy}} C_6H_{12}O_6 + 6O_2$$

Exam tip

You should know the word and symbol equations for photosynthesis.

Try to remember that the gases carbon dioxide and oxygen are involved and they come in alphabetical order. Also water and glucose are in the equation, not in alphabetical order.

Plants make food and either use it to carry out their daily processes or store it for future use. Animals eat plants and so the energy the plants have trapped is passed on in the food chain to the animals. Plants are essential to all life on our planet. They also return oxygen to the atmosphere to be used in respiration.

The glucose made during photosynthesis is transported as soluble sugars to all parts of the plant, where it can be used or stored as insoluble **starch**. Glucose and starch can be converted into other substances that the plant needs. Glucose is:

- used for respiration
- converted to **cellulose** for cell walls
- converted to protein for growth and repair
- converted to starch, **oils** and fats for storage.

The insoluble substances cannot leave the cell: this is why they are used for storage.

In the summer plants grow faster because there is more light and more warmth. This is because they can carry out more photosynthesis. Farmers want photosynthesis to go faster so they can grow more food. Farmers can increase photosynthesis by giving plants more:

- light • carbon dioxide • warmth

How science works

Scientists use technology in glasshouses to adjust the level of these three factors so that they can be carefully controlled to give optimum conditions for maximum growth.

They use heaters to increase the temperature and these give out carbon dioxide so the level of carbon dioxide increases as well.

When it is warm and there is no need for heaters, there is no increase in carbon dioxide.

Limiting factors

If light, carbon dioxide or warmth is in short supply, it becomes a **limiting factor**. This is because a shortage of one of these factors will limit the rate of photosynthesis.

The three graphs show what happens when each factor increases, while the others are kept constant.

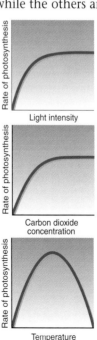

In the first two graphs, initially the rate increases – it then becomes constant even though that factor is still increasing. This is because another factor is in short supply and is limiting the rate. In the third graph the temperature is increasing. This eventually denatures the plant's enzymes and so the rate drops to zero.

Respiration versus photosynthesis

All living organisms including plants respire all of the time. If they do not they die. When they respire they take in oxygen and give out carbon dioxide. Plants also take in carbon dioxide and give out oxygen as they photosynthesise during the day.

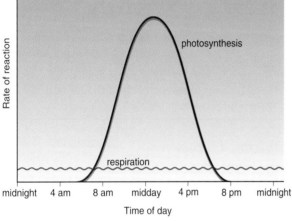

Plants photosynthesise faster than they respire – so during the day they give out more oxygen than they use and absorb more carbon dioxide than they release.

Test yourself

1 Where do the raw materials for photosynthesis come from and what is the energy source?

2 How can a glasshouse in your garden be provided with more light, warmth and carbon dioxide?

3 Look at the graph of respiration and photosynthesis. How does the shape of this graph change at different times of the day? How would the shape be different if the rate was measured in winter?

4 Look at the graph of light intensity against rate of photosynthesis (page 17). Explain what is happening when the curve is going up and when the curve plateaus.

5 Look at the graph of temperature against rate of photosynthesis (page 17). Explain what is happening when the curve is falling.

B2d Compete or die & B2e Adapt to fit

After revising these items you should:

● understand how animals and plants compete with or rely on each other and that changing our environment affects animal and plant distributions.

Competition

Every organism is in **competition** with every other organism. Organisms compete for:

• food   • water   • shelter
• light   • minerals

This competition may affect the distribution and population size of animals and plants.

Competition ensures that the population of any one species does not get too big. When a population does get too big, something usually happens to bring it down again.

Exam tip

You should know how species of organisms compete to survive and breed.

Competition between species

There is also competition between different species. This happens because a habitat can only support so many species. They are competing for the same space and food. The most successful species survive and the least successful ones die. The organisms are competing for the same **ecological niche**, for example:

• red and grey squirrel
• ladybird and harlequin ladybird
• mink and otter.

Predator and prey

Predators and prey both affect the size of each other's population. The graph shows the relationship between the populations of lions (predator) and zebra (prey).

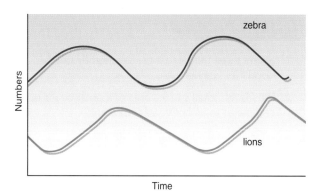

This cyclic relationship helps to maintain the balance in numbers of each species and stops any population increase getting out of control.

Exam tip

You will be expected to describe the patterns you can see in the graph and explain why they are happening.

You may not be familiar with the organisms but the pattern between predator and prey will always be the same.

Parasitism and mutualism

A parasite is an organism that lives on or in another living organism. The organism they live on is the host. The parasite benefits and the host loses.

Parasites of humans include:
- tapeworm • flea

The tapeworm:
- grows in the gut of animals
- feeds off the food the animal eats
- can cause blockage in the host's gut
- can grow up to several metres long.

Fleas suck blood from their host. This can weaken the host and introduce dangerous diseases.

Some organisms live together. Where both organisms benefit from the relationship it is called **mutualism**. The oxpecker bird eats the small parasites that live in the fur of mammals (buffalo). This ensures that the oxpecker survives and is successful and the buffalo gets rid of its parasites.

The close interdependence ensures that when one organism survives and is successful, the other one is too. It determines the distribution and abundance of different organisms in different habitats.

The mutualistic relationship between nitrogen fixing bacteria which live in root nodules of leguminous plants means that the plant has more nitrates and so can make more protein and the bacteria is provided with sugars for food. The bacteria convert atmospheric nitrogen into nitrates which the plants can use to make protein.

Adaptations

Animals are **adapted** to live in their environment. They will have adapted to that environment over a long period of time. This is so they can survive and compete for limited resources.

The more quickly an organism can adapt the more chance it has of survival. How it adapts will also affect its distribution and abundance. For example:
- organisms that have adapted to dry conditions will live in a desert
- those that have adapted to live in water are found in lakes, rivers and the sea.

How is a camel adapted to life in the desert?

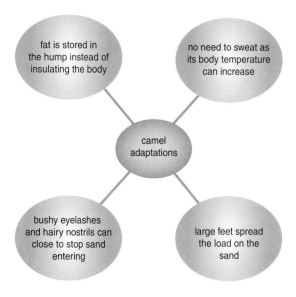

The table shows how a polar bear is adapted to life in the Arctic.

Feature	How it adapts the polar bear
thick fur	for insulation
white fur	for camouflage
layer of fat	for insulation
sharp claws and teeth	to catch and eat prey
strong legs	for running and swimming
large feet	to spread the load on snow
fur on soles of feet	for insulation and grip
small ears	small surface area when compared to body

Plants are also adapted to their environments. The cactus is adapted to hot, dry conditions in these ways:

- Rounded shape gives reduced surface area/ volume ratio to reduce water loss and store water.
- Thick cuticle reduces water loss.
- Leaves reduced to spines reduce water loss and discourage animals.
- Green stem allows photosynthesis.
- Water storage to withstand droughts.
- Long roots reach down to water.

Adaptation for pollination

Pollination is the transfer of pollen from the anther of the stamen to the stigma.

In order to reproduce, plants must be pollinated. So that pollination is successful, plants are adapted to pollination by wind or by insects.

Wind-pollinated plants:	Insect-pollinated plants:
• feathery stigmas • small, light pollen	• colourful petals • sticky pollen • nectar

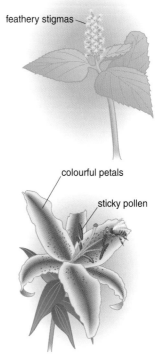

B2f Survival of the fittest

The fossil record

The **fossil** record refers to all the fossils found in different layers of rock. The different layers of rock help scientists to work out the age of the fossil and know which are the oldest and which are the youngest.

Scientists believe that the clues to our origins lie in the fossil record. Animals and plants can change over long periods of time and fossils provide evidence for this. Fossils can give us evidence of organisms that lived long ago.

The fossil record has been interpreted differently over time:

- Creationists, who believe that their God created all life on Earth, believe that God created the fossil record too.

- Most scientists think that the fossil record provides evidence for evolution of life on Earth over millions of years. This makes the Earth much older than when creationists believe God created it (a few thousand years ago).

The fossil record is not complete because:

- some fossils have not yet been discovered
- some organisms do not produce fossils – soft tissue usually decays and does not fossilise
- fossilisation rarely occurs.

How fossils are formed

Fossils form over time in different ways. The boxes show three of these.

A	The hard body parts (shells, bones, leaves) of a dead organism are covered with sediment. These body parts are gradually replaced by minerals which form the fossil.
B	Casts and impressions of the body are made in rock.
C	The body is preserved whole in: • amber • peat bogs • tar pits • ice

The fossil record of a horse's leg has provided information of the evolution of the horse.

The palaeontologist Marsh described three fossil horses he found, Orohippus, Miohippus and Hipparion. As more fossil horses were discovered, it became clear that the evolution of the horse was complicated. The horse evolved to run fast. Early horses ran on four fingers, modern horses run on the middle finger only.

The diagrams show the changes over time of a horse's teeth, legs and body shape.

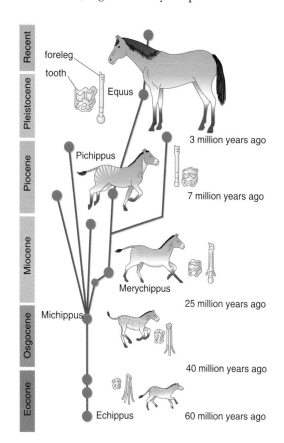

Natural selection

When environments change some animal and plant species survive or evolve but many become **extinct** because they cannot change quickly enough.

Those organisms that are better adapted to their environment are more likely to survive. This is called **natural selection**.

Darwin put forward this theory. It contains several stages.

- Members of the same species are different from each other. This is natural variation.
- Each organism is in competition with every other for limited resources.
- Some are better adapted than others and so survive and reproduce (survival of the fittest).
- The offspring inherit these successful adaptations.
- Those without the successful characteristics die.
- Those unable to compete become extinct.

Over time the changes brought about by natural selection may result in the formation of a new species.

Adaptations are controlled by genes. Genes are passed on to the next generation.

Natural selection is still going on today. Examples include:

- The peppered moth was grey and well camouflaged on the light bark of trees. During the industrial revolution the bark was covered in soot and the moths were no longer hidden. Some moths were slightly darker and more camouflaged so they survived and reproduced. Within a few years all the moths were darker.

Exam tip

*You should be able to explain the occurrence of dark and pale forms of the peppered moth in areas with different levels of **pollution**. There are more dark moths in areas where pollution is higher and more light coloured moths in areas of less pollution.*

- Bacteria are becoming resistant to antibiotics. This is because when antibiotics are used to treat disease, some bacteria survive and breed. Their resistance is passed on to the next generation. Soon they are all resistant.
- Rats are becoming resistant to the rat poison warfarin. Rats are fussy about their food. They eat a little bit. If they like it they will return to eat more. The warfarin will kill some before they return. Those rats that are not killed are resistant to warfarin and survive to breed. Soon all rats are resistant to warfarin and another poison has to be found.

How science works

When we have a bacterial infection, the doctor prescribes antibiotics to kill the bacteria and we get better. But some bacteria may mutate and become resistant.

The doctor can try a different antibiotic but again some bacteria may mutate and become resistant. This leads to multi-resistant strains of bacteria, which are difficult to control and are becoming a big problem in hospitals.

Scientists are currently trying to solve this problem.

Sometimes a population gets separated into two breeding groups. These two populations evolve independently and may not be able to breed with each other. This means they are now two different species.

There are other theories of evolution besides Darwin's. Lamarck's theory of inheritance of acquired characteristics is one of them, but it was discredited because acquired characteristics do not have a genetic basis.

It is important to see all the evidence before coming to a conclusion about a theory. Many new theories have been met with hostility before all the evidence was considered.

1 Fossils give us clues to the origins of life. Explain why the fossil record is incomplete.

2 Look at the diagrams of a horse's leg.

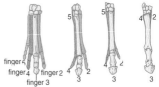

Orohippus   Miohippus   Hipparion   Equus (modern horse)

Describe how the horse's leg has changed over time.

3 (a) Describe the stages in Darwin's theory of evolution.

(b) Explain how Lamarck's theory is different.

4 The sentences describe how antibiotic resistance develops.
They are in the wrong order. Put them in the correct order.

   A   some resistant bacteria survive
   B   some bacteria are killed
   C   soon they are all resistant
   D   antibiotics are given to a person to kill bacteria
   E   their resistance is passed on to the next generation
   F   the surviving resistant bacteria breed

5 Explain how rats have become resistant to warfarin.

B2g Population out of control?

The problem

The human population is increasing. More people means we are using more of the world's **resources** and producing more pollution. If the rate of increase continues the Earth will not be able to sustain all the people living on it. Some countries are already taking steps to slow down the rate of increase. The graph shows how the human population has grown over the last 2000 years.

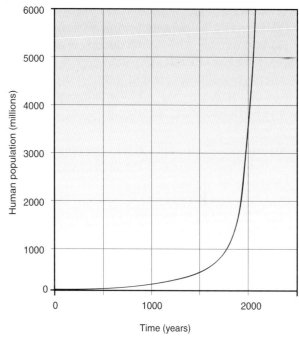

In parts of the world the human population is growing **exponentially**. This means that the population doubles every 53 years. The possible consequences are:

• running out of food

• not enough space

• build up of waste with no space to dispose of it.

Each of these will have a negative impact on the population as a whole.

Pollution

The table shows the population and the amount of carbon dioxide produced by Africa and the USA.

Place	Population (millions)	Carbon dioxide produced (billions of tonnes)
Africa	732	0.4
USA	265	4.9

The developed countries of the world such as the USA have a small proportion of the world's population compared to less developed countries such as those in Africa. But they produce more of the pollutant carbon dioxide and use more of the resources.

As pollution increases the consequences for the world also increase. Effects include:

- global warming from increasing levels of carbon dioxide. The carbon dioxide comes from burning **fossil fuels**. The Sun's energy enters the Earth's atmosphere and warms it up. Carbon dioxide traps this heat and the temperature of the Earth increases. This is called the greenhouse effect.
- **ozone** depletion from CFCs in the upper atmosphere. Ozone is in the upper atmosphere and absorbs the ultraviolet (UV) rays from the Sun. UV rays are harmful to humans. Pollutants like CFCs damage the ozone layer and let in the harmful UV rays.
- **acid rain** from sulfur dioxide. This gas is produced when fossil fuels are burned. It dissolves in rain in the atmosphere and produces an acid. This acid falls as rain. It acidifies lakes and kills fish and trees. Acid rain also dissolves **limestone** and this affects many of our buildings and statues.

How science works

Technological developments have often had damaging effects on our environment. Burning fossil fuels has resulted in acid rain to such an extent that large areas of forest have been destroyed when this falls.

Also the acid water gets into lakes and rivers and kills all of the living organisms. These living organisms could be the food supply of another animal or human population.

Measuring pollution

Pollution can be measured by using living indicators – we call these **indicator species**.

The table shows some indicator species and where they live.

Indicator species	Where they live
bloodworm waterlouse	polluted water (little oxygen)
rat-tailed maggot sludgeworm	very polluted water
lichen	clean air (little air pollution)

Exam tip

You may be given some data, e.g. a map showing the distribution of an indicator species. You should be able to analyse it and draw conclusions.

Test yourself

1 Name three of the Earth's resources that are being used up.

2 What are the possible consequences of the human population increasing exponentially?

3 Explain how burning fossil fuels causes global warming.

4 How does sulfur dioxide in the air contribute to acid rain?

5 Look at the table below. It shows how much sulfur dioxide different lichen species can tolerate.

Lichen	Level of sulfur dioxide tolerated (μg/m³)
no lichens	175
Lechanora sp.	125
Parmelia sp.	50
Usnea sp.	0

(a) What level of sulfur dioxide stops lichens growing?
(b) Suggest which lichen(s) will grow where sulfur dioxide levels are 50 μg/m³?

B2h Sustainability

After revising this item you should:

- understand why organisms become extinct, explain how endangered species can be protected, explain sustainable development and understand what choices we have to achieve this.

Endangered and extinct

When all the individuals in a species die, the species becomes extinct. Extinction can happen naturally as a result of **climate change** or by competition with another species.

A species that is likely to become extinct is an **endangered** species.

There are several reasons why an organism may become extinct:

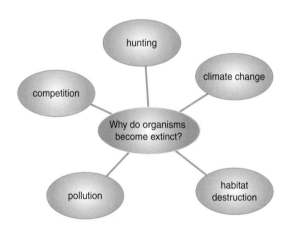

- When humans develop areas of the countryside, they destroy the habitats of some organisms. If that is the only place in the world where those organisms live they will become extinct.
- Humans hunt animals to eat or for their skin. This can reduce the numbers so much that they become an endangered species.
- Humans pollute the environment of living organisms so that they can no longer live there. They must move or die.

We are responsible for many of these problems so what can we do to help the situation?

protecting habitats	Protect habitats that contain rare or endangered species. Sites of Special Scientific Interest can be set up to prevent the land being developed.
education	Teach people about the organisms and their habitat and how important it is to look after it.
legal protection	Laws make it illegal to harm certain species.
captive breeding programmes	Breed rare and endangered species in captivity and then release them back into the environment.
artificial ecosystems	Create new ecosystems for endangered species to live in.

Conservation

The more we look after our environment, the more species will survive. The more species there are in any one habitat, the more likely it is to survive, and small changes in the habitat can usually be accommodated. There are many reasons for conserving our environment:

- To protect the human food supply. If we damage our environment we put our food supply at risk.
- To discover new plants that could provide us with medicines in the future.
- To minimise damage to food chains and webs, so other organisms can find food.
- To look after endangered species.
- To preserve our cultural heritage for future generations.

Sustainable development

When we remove something from our environment, we should replace it to protect that environment. This is called **sustainable development**.

As the world population grows, more and more resources are being used up. The demand for food and energy is constantly growing. We are producing more waste products and we have less land to dispose of them.

In order to maintain this growing population, feed them and dispose of their waste, we must encompass sustainable development.

Educating the public plays an important part in sustaining our environment and protecting endangered species for future generations.

The table shows how we can replace some of those things we remove – and so sustain our resources.

Removed item	How to replace
cut down trees	replant with young trees so that when they grow they can be cut down
fish	introduce quotas so that fish stocks do not get too low
	limit the minimum size of fish that can be caught so that the young ones have a chance to grow and reproduce

Sustainable development may protect endangered species by replacing those individuals that have been killed. For example, where forests are cut down to provide wood, we should plant new trees so that there will be trees for future generations to use.

Whales

These mammals have commercial value both during their lives and when dead.

- Alive – attract tourists and bring in money.
- Dead – bodies are used for food, oil and cosmetics.

Scientists still have a lot to learn about whales. For example:

- how they survive at extreme depths
- how they communicate over long distances
- their migration patterns from one part of the world to another to find food or a mate.

How science works

International cooperation is needed to protect the whales from those who hunt them. But whales live far out in the oceans – and it is difficult to enforce laws on whaling because they are usually found in international waters.

Some countries, e.g. Japan, continue whaling, claiming they do it for scientific research reasons.

Some whales are bred and live in captivity. Their behaviour is studied by scientists who try to understand more about them. They are also used as entertainment in aquariums.

Test yourself

1 Trees are being felled in tropical rainforests. Scientists have noticed that there are fewer types of animals and plants in these deforested regions. Explain why.

2 List the ways in which humans can help endangered species.

3 Why is the panda an endangered species?

4 Explain how cutting down trees and replanting more trees is an example of sustainable development.

5 Whales are kept in captivity for human research and entertainment. Give one reason for and one reason against each of these uses.

B3a Molecules of life

After revising this item you should:

- be able to explain that respiration takes place in mitochondria of cells, understand the structure of DNA and its role in the production of proteins and understand how enzymes work.

Mitochondria

Organisms are made up of cells. Cells are very small and can only be seen using a microscope. Microscopes have been improved and we can see more and more detail.

Using an electron microscope, we can see the **mitochondria**.

These are the site of respiration.

Respiration provides energy for all life processes.

Mitochondria contain enzymes that carry out the final stages of respiration.

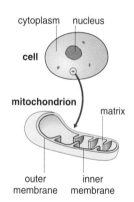

Proteins

Proteins are made up of chains of amino acids. The amino acids each cell uses come from the protein in our diet.

Some foods do not contain all the amino acids we need. The liver can change some amino acids into others (transamination). But essential amino acids must be obtained from our food.

Each protein has its own number and sequence of amino acids. This results in different shaped molecules which have different functions. For example:

- enzymes are folded into a compact 3D shape
- structural proteins are longer and often wound into a triple helix to give more strength.

The cell's nucleus controls which proteins the cell makes (protein synthesis). The instructions for this are carried in the code of DNA bases in the nucleus.

DNA

Chromosomes in the nucleus are made of DNA. DNA is made of two strands of organic bases twisted into a spiral. This is called a **double helix**.

Between the two strands are cross-links formed by two of the bases.

The structure of DNA.

There are four bases altogether: A, T, C and G. They pair up in a specific way, which we call **complementary base pairing**.

The diagrams show the structure of DNA and how the bases are arranged.

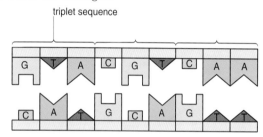

Strand of DNA showing detail of bases.

The order of bases codes for the order of amino acids in a protein.

- Each amino acid is coded by a sequence of three bases called the triplet code.
- The total sequence of bases that codes for a protein is a gene.
- The number of triplets in one gene varies.

The DNA can copy itself (DNA replication) and does this before a cell divides.

1. The two strands 'unzip' to form single strands.
2. New bases join up with the exposed bases by complementary base pairing.
3. Two complete double strands are formed.

Each new strand is identical to the original.

After **fertilisation** there is one fertilised egg cell. The DNA in the nucleus of this cell copies itself and the cell divides into two. Each new cell has identical DNA. This process continues until there are millions of cells in an adult.

DNA fingerprints

The DNA of each person is unique and can be used to identify a person. To do this a DNA fingerprint must be made. The stages in making a DNA fingerprint are:

1 Isolate DNA from cells.

2 Fragment DNA.

3 Separate the DNA fragments by electrophoresis.

4 Compare with a reference sample.

This process is shown in the next diagram.

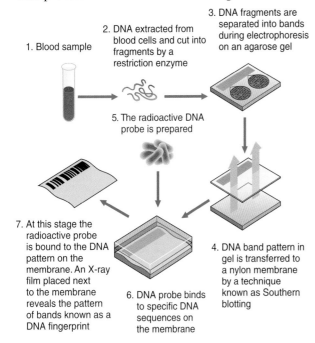

1. Blood sample

2. DNA extracted from blood cells and cut into fragments by a restriction enzyme

3. DNA fragments are separated into bands during electrophoresis on an agarose gel

5. The radioactive DNA probe is prepared

7. At this stage the radioactive probe is bound to the DNA pattern on the membrane. An X-ray film placed next to the membrane reveals the pattern of bands known as a DNA fingerprint

6. DNA probe binds to specific DNA sequences on the membrane

4. DNA band pattern in gel is transferred to a nylon membrane by a technique known as Southern blotting

How science works

Forensic scientists use DNA fingerprinting to:
- confirm a suspect was at a crime scene
- confirm a suspect was not at a crime scene
- prove or disprove a parent of a child.

Enzymes

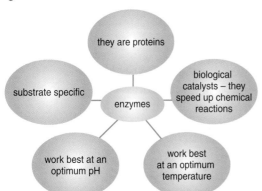

they are proteins

substrate specific

enzymes

biological catalysts – they speed up chemical reactions

work best at an optimum pH

work best at an optimum temperature

Each enzyme catalyses one reaction only. It is highly specific to a single substrate.

Each protein has its own number and sequence of amino acids. This results in different shaped enzyme molecules which have different functions.

The specificity of an enzyme is explained by the way it works.

- The chemical it reacts with is the **substrate**.
- The substrate fits into the **active site** of the enzyme.
- The shape of the active site means that only a substrate that has a complementary shape can fit into it – similar to a lock and key.

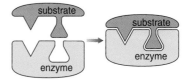

substrate

enzyme

substrate

enzyme

Optimum temperature and pH

An enzyme works best at one, optimum temperature.

- Below this temperature the rate of reaction is slower, but the enzyme still works if the temperature rises again.
- Above this temperature the rate slows down and stops.

An enzyme works best at one pH. Above or below the optimum pH the structure of the enzyme is changed.

High temperatures and extremes of pH will change the shape of the enzyme's active site. Once changed, it cannot regain the correct shape and so the enzyme cannot catalyse reactions. It is said to be **denatured**.

The following graphs show the effect of changing temperature and pH on the rate of an enzyme-controlled reaction.

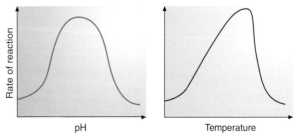

Rate of reaction

pH

Temperature

Most enzymes work best at body temperature (37°C) and at a specific pH, which is different for each enzyme.

Test yourself

1 The table shows the sequence of three bases for four amino acids.

Sequence of three bases	Amino acid
CGT	P
CAA	Q
CAG	R
GTA	S

Look at the strand of DNA showing the base sequence (page 27).

(a) Give the order of amino acids that the bases in the upper strand code for.

(b) If the last base A was changed to G, would the amino acids be different? If so, how would they be different?

2 Describe complementary base pairing.

3 Name three chemical reactions in a living cell that are catalysed by enzymes.

4 Mary washed the football team's shirts after a match. They had lots of grass stains on them. She used a biological washing powder and washed the shirts at 100°C but the stains did not come out. Explain why.

5 The DNA fingerprints shown are those of a mother, child and possible father.

(a) Is this the father of the child?

(b) Explain your answer.

B3b Diffusion

After revising this item you should:

- be able to explain how materials move through living organisms by diffusion, understand where diffusion occurs in animal and plant cells and explain the importance of diffusion in these cells.

Moving particles

Inside our bodies substances move in and out of cells by diffusion through the cell membrane.

Diffusion is:

- the movement of a substance from an area of its high concentration to an area of its low concentration along a **concentration gradient**.

It is the net movement of particles.

- Particles move from high to low concentration and from low to high concentration but overall more move from high to low.

- Each particle is constantly moving at random and tends to spread out.

The diagram shows the useful substances a cell gains and the waste products it gets rid of by diffusion.

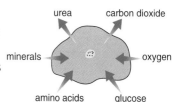

The rate of diffusion is increased by:

- a shorter diffusion distance
- a greater difference in concentration (gradient)
- a larger surface area.

Diffusion in animals

The following table gives some examples of diffusion in animals.

Where diffusion occurs	What diffuses	From where	To where
small intestine	digested food	**lumen** of small intestine	blood
lungs	oxygen	air in **alveoli**	blood
lungs	carbon dioxide	blood	air in alveoli
placenta	digested food and oxygen	mother's blood	fetal blood
placenta	carbon dioxide and waste	fetal blood	mother's blood
synapse	chemical **transmitter substances**	end of a neurone	beginning of another neurone

Each body part is adapted as follows:

1   Alveoli in lungs for efficient gaseous exchange.
- **Permeable**.   • Moist.
- Large surface area.   • Good blood supply.
- Alveoli wall one cell thick.

Exam tip

Avoid the mistake of saying 'cell wall is one cell thick' – remember that animal cells do not have cell walls, only cell membranes.

2   Small intestine for food absorption.
- Long.
- Large surface area (**villi** and **microvilli**).
- Permeable surface.
- Good blood supply.

3   Placenta to increase the rate of diffusion to the **fetus**.
- Large surface area.   • Villi.
- Good blood supply.

4   The synapse, which transmitter substances diffuse across to carry signals from one neurone to the next.
- Transmitter substances are only produced on one side of the synapse.
- They are in high concentration on one side and low concentration on the other.
- The gap is tiny.

Diffusion in plants

The following table gives some examples of diffusion in plants.

Where diffusion occurs	What diffuses	From where	To where
leaves	oxygen and carbon dioxide	stomata/air	air/ stomata
leaves	water vapour	leaf (intercellular spaces)	air

The leaves are adapted to increase the rate of carbon dioxide and oxygen diffusion:
- They have **stomata** on their bottom surface.
- They are flat and thin to give a large surface area.
- There are air spaces inside the leaves.

Plants use oxygen and produce carbon dioxide during respiration, which takes place in all plant cells both day and night. In addition they use carbon dioxide and produce oxygen during photosynthesis during the day.

Test yourself

1   Describe one way in which the surface area of a cell can be increased.

2   What are villi and microvilli? What part do they play in absorption?

3   List the features that all diffusion surfaces have in common.

4   During which part of the day does diffusion take place in plants?

5   Natasha used some perfume at the back of the laboratory. Students sitting near her complained about the smell but the teacher at the front ignored them – she could smell nothing. Explain why the students could smell the perfume but the teacher could not.

B3c Keep it moving

After revising this item you should:

- be able to explain how parts of the blood are adapted for their function, understand how the circulatory system works and explain the problems of replacing hearts with transplants and artificial parts.

Blood

The blood is made up of:
- **red blood cells**
- **white blood cells**
- **plasma**.

Red blood cells are well adapted to carry out their function.

Red blood cell adaptation	How this helps with its function
small size	can fit through narrow blood vessels
bi-concave disc shape	gives a large surface area to volume ratio to gain or lose oxygen more quickly
no nucleus	more **haemoglobin** can fit in the cell
contains haemoglobin	combines with oxygen to form **oxyhaemoglobin** in the lungs, and gives up the oxygen in the tissues

White blood cells:

- are bigger than red blood cells
- have a flexible shape to engulf disease organisms.

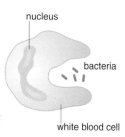

Plasma is the liquid part of the blood which carries cells and substances around the body.

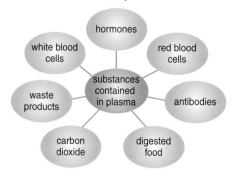

Circulatory system

The circulatory system consists of the heart and the blood vessels.

The parts work together to transport substances around the body.

- **Arteries** transport blood away from the heart.
- **Veins** transport blood to the heart.
- **Capillaries** are involved in exchange of substances in the tissues.

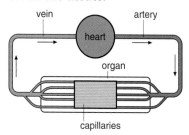

Exam tip

Remember that:

- *Arteries carry oxygenated blood – except the pulmonary artery.*
- *Veins carry deoxygenated blood – except the pulmonary vein.*

The following table shows how blood vessels are adapted for their role in carrying blood to and from the heart.

Arteries	Veins	Capillaries
thick, muscular and elastic wall – withstands high pressure	• large lumen – eases blood flow • valves – prevent backflow of blood	walls are one cell thick and permeable – allows for rapid diffusion of glucose and oxygen to the tissues and carbon dioxide and waste from the tissues

The heart

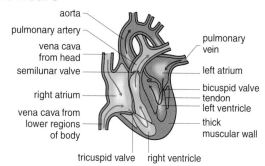

The following table shows the functions of the main parts of the heart.

Part	Function
right **atrium**	to receive blood from the body and pass it to the right ventricle
left atrium	to receive blood from the lungs and pass it to the left ventricle
right **ventricle**	to receive blood from the right atrium and pump it to the lungs
left ventricle	to receive blood from the left atrium and to pump it to the body
valves – **semilunar, bicuspid, tricuspid**	to stop blood flowing backwards
four blood vessels – **vena cava, pulmonary artery**, pulmonary vein, **aorta**	to take blood into or out of the heart

The left ventricle wall is thicker than the right ventricle wall because it pumps blood all round the body – the right ventricle only pumps blood as far as the lungs.

> ### Exam tip
>
> *You need to know where each structure is and what it does. Try adding labels in the correct places to an unlabelled diagram of the heart.*
>
> *Remember also that:*
> - *vena cava is a vein, aorta is an artery*
> - *chambers of the heart contract to push blood*
> - *valves stop backflow of blood.*

Mammals have a **double circulatory** system. Blood has to pass through the heart twice on each full circuit of the body.

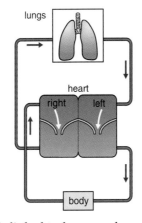

This means that higher pressures can be established so more blood flows to the tissues.

Cholesterol

The amount of **cholesterol** in the arteries is linked to how much cholesterol is in the food you eat.

Cholesterol builds up in the arteries to form a **plaque**, which can restrict blood flow or cause a blockage.

Heart problems

If the blockage is in an artery supplying the heart muscle (coronary artery), then part of the heart is starved of oxygen and dies. This can cause a heart attack.

This can be remedied by a heart transplant. However, there can be many problems with the supply of donor hearts for transplant:

- There is a shortage of donor hearts.
- Tissues must match.
- Blood groups must be the same.
- The size should be the same.
- The age of donor and recipient should be the same.

There is also the risk that the recipient's body will reject the donor heart. Heart patients have to take anti-rejection drugs and other drugs for the rest of their life.

Mechanical replacements, such as artificial pacemakers and valves, can be used instead. But these can have other problems:

- Unsuitable size of parts.
- A power supply is needed.
- The body may react to the artificial parts.

The following table summarises the advantages and disadvantages of artificial pacemakers and valves compared with transplants.

Advantages	Disadvantages
readily available – no wait for suitable donor heart no need for anti-rejection drugs	pacemaker needs a battery which must be replaced regularly mechanical valves can go wrong difficult to get parts in the right sizes materials can cause allergic reactions harder for a pacemaker to change its rate during exercise than a transplant heart

> ### Test yourself
>
> 1. Where does the pulmonary artery carry blood from and to?
>
> 2. The diagram shows sections through two arteries A and B.
>
>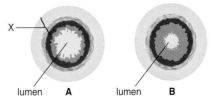
>
>   (a) Which artery shows a build up of cholesterol? How does cholesterol affect the circulation?
>   (b) What does X represent? How would X be different in a vein?
>
> 3. Explain how a red blood cell is adapted to carry oxygen around the body.
>
> 4. A fish has a single circulation. Its blood passes through the heart to the gills, then to the body and back to the heart. How is the double circulation of a human different to this?
>
> 5. Why is a heart transplant better than a pacemaker if the patient wants to do a lot of exercise?

B3d Divide and rule & B3e Growing up

After revising these items you should:

- be able to explain mitosis and meiosis, understand the advantages of being a multicellular organism and understand the main phases of human growth.

Cell division

Cells can divide in one of two ways:

- **Mitosis** – allows growth and specialisation of cells in an organism.
- **Meiosis** – produces **gametes** (eggs and sperm) during sexual reproduction.

Mitosis allows organisms to grow by increasing the number of cells. It leads to **multicellular** organisms. The advantages of being multicellular are shown in the following spider diagram.

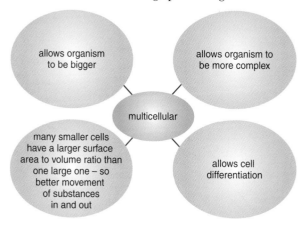

Mitosis

In mammals, body cells are **diploid** (they have two of each chromosome). Human body cells contain 46 chromosomes in 23 pairs.

During mitosis:

- the chromosomes are copied
- the copies divide and move to opposite poles of the cell
- each new cell is genetically identical to the original one.

a cell has four chromosomes, two pairs

chromosomes are copied

chromosomes from one line down the centre of the cell

one copy of each chromosome moves to the opposite pole of the cell

Mitosis.

Meiosis

Meiosis produces gametes (sex cells). It occurs only in the sex organs.

Gametes are **haploid** – they contain one of each chromosome. Gametes join at fertilisation to produce a diploid **zygote**.

As any sperm can fertilise any egg, the possible combinations of chromosomes is endless. This produces variation.

During meiosis:

- chromosomes are copied and the copies stay together
- the pairs of chromosomes then separate and move to opposite poles of the cell
- the cell divides to form two cells
- each chromosome copy divides to opposite poles of the cell
- the two cells divide again
- the number of chromosomes is halved in each new cell.

a cell has four chromosomes, two pairs

chromosome are copied

chromosome pairs line up side by side

the copies split to produce four cells, each containing half the original number of chromosomes

Meiosis.

The following diagram shows that a sperm cell is adapted to its function.

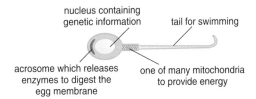

Growing up

All plants and animals are made of one or more cells.

Animal cells contain:

- nucleus
- membrane
- cytoplasm

Plant cells contain:

- nucleus
- membrane
- cytoplasm
- chloroplasts
- cell wall
- large vacuole

The following table shows the difference in growth of animals and plants.

Animals	Plants
grow to a finite size	grow continuously
cells stop growing at a certain size	greater enlargement of cells means they can grow to greater heights
cell division happens over the whole body	cell division happens at tips of roots and shoots
lose ability to **differentiate** at an early stage	retain the ability to differentiate

Some cells produced by mitosis are undifferentiated. Undifferentiated cells are called **stem cells**. These cells can develop into different cells tissues and organs. Examples in animals are muscle and blood cells.

How science works

Scientific research shows that stem cells can be used to grow different types of cells in the laboratory. These cells could be used to provide replacement parts for human organs that no longer function. The stem cells usually come from an embryo.

Write down one argument supporting stem cell research and one against it.

Human growth

Humans start growing at fertilisation. The **gestation period** is the time of growth between fertilisation and birth.

The gestation period is different for other mammals. Usually, the larger the animal, the longer the gestation period.

During gestation parts of the body grow at different rates. The next diagram shows the relative growth of body parts of a human.

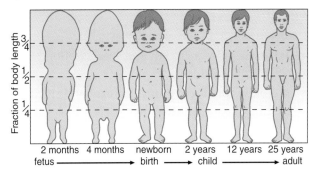

The graphs show data on weight and head size in babies. The data can provide doctors with early warnings of growth problems.

If a baby's measurements fall inside the normal range then there is no cause for concern.

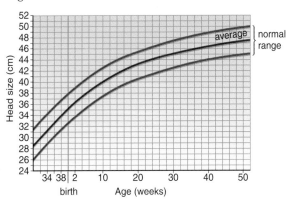

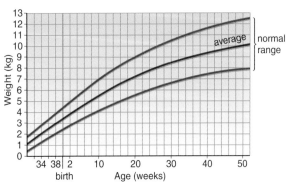

B3f Controlling plant growth & B3g New genes for old

Plant hormones

Plants show growth responses to light and gravity.

Response	Result
positive	plant grows **towards** an environmental stimulus
negative	plant grows **away** from an environmental stimulus

Part of plant	Response to light	Response to gravity
shoot	positively phototropic	negatively geotropic
root	negatively phototropic	positively geotropic

The main hormone plants produce is **auxin**. Plants respond to hormones produced as a result of environmental stimuli – these growth responses are called tropisms.

The diagram shows how auxin affects growth.

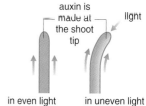

auxin is made at the shoot tip   light

in even light the auxin passes down the shoot and causes even growth

in uneven light the auxin causes more growth on the shaded side of the shoot

Auxin made in the tip of the shoot diffuses away from the tip. It causes the cells to grow more and become elongated.

- In even light, auxin causes even growth so the shoot grows straight upwards.
- In uneven light, auxin accumulates on the shaded side of the shoot. Cells on this side grow more than cells on the light side so the shoot curves towards the light.

Horticulturalists use **plant hormones** to improve their crops. Scientists have produced artificial hormones which mimic the real ones.

The commercial uses of hormones include:

- **selective weedkillers** to kill only the unwanted plants
- **rooting powders** to encourage root growth in cuttings
- fruit ripening so that fruit can be picked unripe and ripened during transportation
- control of **dormancy** so that plants can be produced on demand.

How science works

There is greater demand for flowers at special times of the year, e.g. Mother's Day. Scientists have used developments in plant hormone knowledge to achieve flowering whenever they want.

plant hormones

- involved in the plant's response to gravity (**geotropism**)
- made in the tips of roots and shoots
- move through the plant in solution
- involved in the plant's response to light (**phototropism**)
- unequally distributed in response to light

Mutation

Mutations are changes to genes. They can be beneficial but most are harmful. A mutation changes the DNA base sequence in the gene. This changes or prevents the production of the protein the gene normally codes for.

The causes of mutations include:

- radiation
- chemicals

or they may occur spontaneously.

Normally mutations occur at a very slow rate.

Humans cannot change the genes of organisms by causing mutations – the results would be random. Instead we have been genetically modifying organisms:

- by selective breeding over thousands of years, and
- more recently, using genetic engineering.

Selective breeding

We can use **selective breeding** to choose favourable characteristics in a plant or animal.

The process involves these stages:

1. Select the desired characteristic, e.g. horses that run fast, sheep with more wool.
2. Choose a male and a female with the desired characteristic and breed them together. (If they come from different species we call this **cross-breeding**.)
3. Choose two of the offspring with the desired characteristic and breed them together.
4. Repeat the process for many generations until the animal with the desired characteristic is produced.

Selective breeding over many generations can create problems:

- A reduction in the gene pool and less variation.
- Repeated **inbreeding** can lead to an accumulation of harmful recessive characteristics.

Genetic engineering

Scientists can transfer genes from one living organism to another to give the recipient organism new characteristics. This is called **genetic engineering** (or genetic modification).

The following table shows the principles of genetic engineering, with an example.

Principle	Example – insulin production
select characteristic	identify the insulin gene
isolate gene	isolate the gene from a human chromosome
insert gene	insert human insulin gene into a bacterium
replicate	the bacterium replicates and makes more bacteria containing the insulin gene
	the bacteria produce human insulin

The diagram shows these principles.

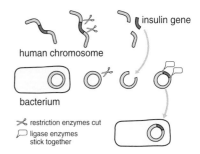

Another example of genetic engineering is taking genes from carrots that control beta-carotene production and putting them into rice. Humans eat rice and can convert the beta-carotene in the rice into Vitamin A.

This means that people in those parts of the world where the diet is lacking in Vitamin A, can now get the vitamin from their diet.

Benefits and risks of genetic engineering

There are both advantages and risks to moving genes between organisms. For example it allows us to produce organisms with new features that are useful to humans. But an inserted gene could have unexpected harmful effects.

Benefits:	Risks:
• We can produce organisms with desired characteristics quickly.	• Inserted genes may have harmful effects on the organism.
• We can modify plants to be resistant to disease, frost damage or to be **pesticide** resistant.	• Genes may be harmful to the environment if they escape.
• We can produce chemicals needed by humans (e.g. insulin) without the need to kill animals.	• Potential side effects of genetically modified food on human health.

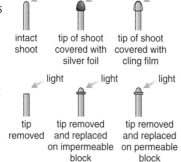
B3h More of the same

Cloning animals

A **clone** is a genetically identical copy of an organism.

Identical twins are naturally occurring clones. So are organisms produced by asexual reproduction.

One way humans can clone animals is by using embryo transplants. This has been done in cows. The process copies what happens when identical twins are produced.

The offspring will be identical to each other but not to either of the parents. This is because the original fertilised egg came from sexual reproduction, so there is a mixture of genes from both parents.

The diagram below shows the steps involved in cloning cows.

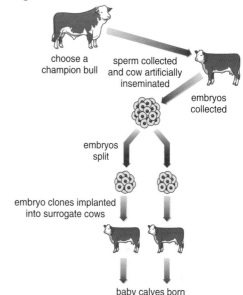

choose a champion bull | sperm collected and cow artificially inseminated | embryos collected

embryos split

embryo clones implanted into surrogate cows

baby calves born

The first mammal to be cloned from an adult mammal was Dolly the sheep in 1996. The diagram below shows the method used to clone Dolly.

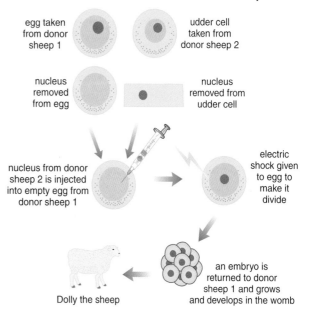

egg taken from donor sheep 1 | udder cell taken from donor sheep 2

nucleus removed from egg | nucleus removed from udder cell

nucleus from donor sheep 2 is injected into empty egg from donor sheep 1 | electric shock given to egg to make it divide

Dolly the sheep | an embryo is returned to donor sheep 1 and grows and develops in the womb

The following table shows some of the issues involved in animal cloning.

Benefits:
- Stem cells could be used for treating illness.
- Animals could be used as a supply of organs for transplant.

Risks:
- If all the animals are identical they could all be killed by one pathogenic organism.
- Animal diseases could spread to humans.
- The practice could lead to human cloning.

The possibility of cloning humans raises ethical dilemmas:
- It would involve killing human embryos, which some people believe is unacceptable.
- Would the cloned child, with the same genes as someone else, be a true individual?

Cloning plants

Plant cloning has been happening for thousands of years.
- Some plants make clones of themselves by asexual reproduction, e.g. the spider plant.
- Gardeners take cuttings of plants to produce new ones.

A more modern method of cloning uses **tissue culture**:
1. Select a plant for a specific characteristic.
2. Cut the plant into many small pieces.
3. Grow pieces on suitable growth medium, containing correct nutrients.
4. Use sterile conditions to avoid infection (**aseptic technique**).
5. Pieces grow into new plants that are genetically identical to the original one.

The following table shows the advantages and disadvantages of producing cloned plants commercially.

Advantages	Disadvantages
you know what you are going to get because all the plants will be genetically identical to each other and to the parent	the population of plants will be genetically very similar – there will be little variety
you can mass produce plants that do not flower very often or are difficult to grow from seeds	because the plants are very similar, a disease or change in the environment could wipe out all of them

Plant cloning is easier than animal cloning because many plant cells retain the ability to differentiate (develop into different types of cells). Animal cells usually lose this ability at a very early stage.

B4a Who planted that there?

Leaf structure

Leaves are all different shapes, sizes and colours. However, they all:

● have the same basic structure

● carry out photosynthesis – their main job.

Although leaves have many colours they all contain the green pigment **chlorophyll**. This traps sunlight and produces food for the plant.

Leaves vary in colour because of the combination of different pigments. In autumn, chlorophyll is the first pigment to break down, which reveals the other pigments: red, orange and yellow. This is why the leaves have so many different colours during this season.

The following diagram shows the internal structure of a thin section of a leaf.

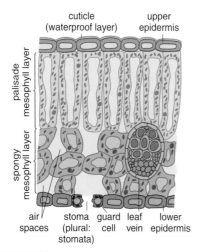

cuticle (waterproof layer), upper epidermis, palisade mesophyll layer, spongy mesophyll layer, air spaces, stoma (plural: stomata), guard cell, leaf vein, lower epidermis

There are no cells in the **cuticle**. It is a layer of wax which helps to prevent water loss.

Under the cuticle are different layers of cells. Every cell in these layers has the same features as a typical plant cell. Some cells have chloroplasts which contain chlorophyll to trap sunlight energy.

Leaves and photosynthesis

The raw materials for photosynthesis are:

● carbon dioxide – from the air

● water – from the soil.

Photosynthesis produces a sugar called glucose. This is:

● used for respiration

● converted into other substances for storage or use in the cell.

Photosynthesis also produces oxygen, which is released to the air or used in respiration.

Leaves are adapted in many ways for photosynthesis. The table shows this.

Feature	Adaptation
broad	gives large surface area to absorb sunlight
thin	provides short distance for gases to diffuse
chloroplasts	they contain chlorophyll to trap sunlight
veins	help to support the leaf and transport substances around it
stomata	allow gases to diffuse in and out through the **lower epidermis**

Efficient photosynthesis

The leaf is also adapted at the cellular level to improve the efficiency of photosynthesis.

Structure	Adaptation
transparent **upper epidermis** (no chloroplasts)	allows light to pass straight through to the **palisade mesophyll** layer below
palisade mesophyll is near the top	contains the most chloroplasts to trap light energy and photosynthesise
air spaces in the **spongy mesophyll**	allows diffusion of gases between the stomata and the photosynthesising cells in the mesophyll layers
very large internal surface area to volume ratio	gives more surface area for absorption of carbon dioxide from air spaces
guard cells	control the opening and closing of stomata for the entry and release of gases

How science works

Some organisms can produce food without photosynthesising – they use hydrogen sulphide instead of water. Scientists are hoping to use them to produce food in the future.

Test yourself

1 How do the products of photosynthesis get to the rest of the plant?

2 In what parts of the leaf does diffusion take place?

3 Look at the diagram of the internal structure of a leaf (page 39).

   (a) Why are there no chloroplasts in the upper epidermis?

   (b) Where does most photosynthesis take place? Give a reason for your answer.

   (c) Which layer allows the gases to circulate? Give a reason for your answer.

4 Explain why trees with needles are not as efficient at photosynthesis as those with broad leaves.

B4b Water, water everywhere

After revising this item you should:

- be able to explain osmosis, understand the role of water movement and transpiration in plants and explain how a plant attempts to reduce water loss.

Osmosis

Osmosis is a special type of diffusion.

Osmosis is:

- the net movement of water molecules (water molecules move in both directions but more move in one direction than the other)
- from an area of high water concentration (dilute solution)
- to an area of low water concentration (concentrated solution)
- across a **partially permeable** membrane
- due to the random movement of particles.

A high concentration of water is usually referred to as a high water potential.

A partially permeable membrane is one that allows certain substances (small water molecules) to pass across it, but not others (large molecules).

The following diagram shows the molecular movement in osmosis.

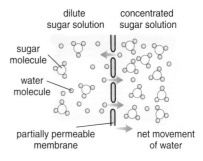

Exam tip

Make sure you understand that dilute solutions contain high water concentrations and vice versa. Think about adding water to concentrated squash to dilute it.

Predicting osmosis

You can predict which way water molecules will move if you know the concentrations of the solutions on either side of a partially permeable membrane.

The following diagram shows two sugar solutions separated by dialysis tubing. As the solution in the beaker contains more water, the water will leave the beaker and pass into the funnel.

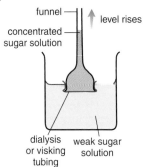

funnel
level rises
concentrated sugar solution
dialysis or visking tubing
weak sugar solution

Water is important to plants because it helps to support them.

- The contents of the turgid cells push against the inelastic cell walls.
- This turgor pressure helps to support the cell.
- When there is little or no turgor pressure, the plant **wilts**.

When plants cells are full of water, the cells are **turgid**. When the plant wilts and the cells are short of water they are **flaccid**.

If a plant loses too much water, the cell membrane may pull away from the cell wall. We call this **plasmolysis**. A plasmolysed cell cannot return to being turgid and usually dies.

Water movement and transpiration

The diagram opposite shows the stages in water movement through a plant.

Transpiration is the loss of water vapour from a leaf. Leaves have to open their stomata to allow gases in and out for efficient photosynthesis. Water diffuses out as well.

The rate of transpiration changes when environmental conditions change.

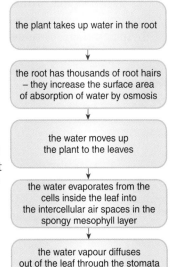

the plant takes up water in the root

↓

the root has thousands of root hairs – they increase the surface area of absorption of water by osmosis

↓

the water moves up the plant to the leaves

↓

the water evaporates from the cells inside the leaf into the intercellular air spaces in the spongy mesophyll layer

↓

the water vapour diffuses out of the leaf through the stomata (when they are open)

Transpiration provides plants with water for:

- cooling (as evaporation needs heat energy which comes from the leaf)
- photosynthesis (water is a raw material)
- support (turgor pressure)
- movement of **minerals** (dissolved in the water).

Plants and their leaves function well when they are turgid, so they try not to lose excessive water. The leaf structure helps with this. It has:

- a waxy cuticle
- few stomata on the upper surface (where evaporation is greatest)
- control over the opening of the stomata.

Stomata

The stomata have two guard cells on either side. These can change their shape and open or close the pore (stoma) between them.

They work like this:

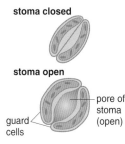

stoma closed

stoma open

pore of stoma (open)

guard cells

- When there is a lot of light, and plenty of water, the guard cells take in water and become turgid. The inner walls of the guard cells bend and the stoma opens.
- In low light, or with water in short supply, the opposite happens and the stoma closes.

Plants that live in the desert have very few stomata on both leaf surfaces, to minimise water loss in the dry desert conditions. The size of the stomata is usually small when compared to plants that live where water is readily available.

Animal cells and water

Animal cells also take in water by osmosis.

- If they take in too much water the cell membrane bursts, as they lack the inelastic cell wall to resist the pressure. This is called **lysis**.
- If they lose too much water, they shrivel up. This is **crenation**.

Test yourself

1 Explain how osmosis is different to diffusion.

2 Why do cooks put cleaned vegetables in water during preparation?

3 A plant wilts after it is dug up and replanted. Which structures must have been removed?

4 Ben weighs three identical pieces of celery and places them into three different solutions. After four hours he takes them out, blots them dry and weighs them again. Ben finds that one is heavier, one is lighter and one remains the same mass.
   (a) Name the process that had taken place.
   (b) Explain why the pieces of celery have different masses.

5 Where in a potato is the partially permeable membrane that water passes through during osmosis?

B4c Transport in plants & B4d Plants need minerals too

After revising these items you should:

- be able to explain the structure and arrangement of xylem and phloem, explain how different factors change the rate of transpiration, understand what plants need minerals for and explain what happens if they are short of these minerals.

How are materials transported?

The plant has two transport systems:

- The **xylem**.
- The **phloem**.

The following diagram shows how the xylem and the phloem are arranged in a leaf, stem and root.

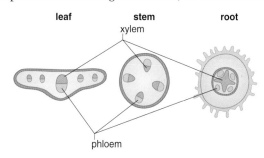

Exam tip

In the stem and root, xylem is always in the middle.

Water always moves up the xylem. Dissolved sugars can move up or down the phloem. The movement of sugars in the phloem is called **translocation**.

Xylem vessels and phloem tubes run continuously throughout the leaves, stems and roots of a plant. In the stem they are gathered together into clusters called **vascular bundles**.

What is transported?

Plants transport many different materials up and down their stems and roots. The table shows some of these and their movements.

What is transported	What is it transported in	Where is it picked up	Where is it going
water	xylem vessels	roots (from the soil)	shoots and leaves
minerals	xylem vessels	roots (dissolved in water from the soil)	shoots and leaves
sugar	phloem tubes	leaves or storage areas	growing and storage tissues

These tissues are specially designed to carry out their functions:

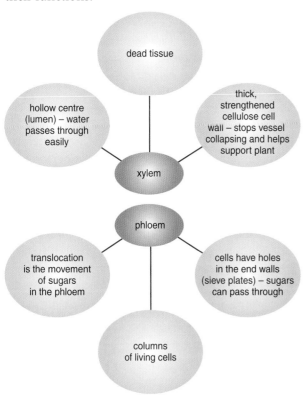

Transpiration rate

During transpiration, water evaporates into the air spaces in the leaf and diffuses out through the stomata. Transpiration creates a suction force that helps to pull more water up through the xylem vessels from the roots.

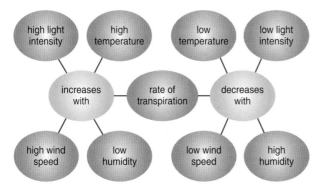

Transpiration rate increases with:	Why it increases?
increased light intensity	there is more photosynthesis so the stomata are open for gas exchange and water diffuses out
increased temperature	molecules have more kinetic energy so evaporate faster
increase in air movement	if it is windy water vapour gets blown away so the concentration gradient is maintained and more vapour diffuses out
decrease in humidity (linked to increased air movement)	the concentration gradient allows more vapour to diffuse out

Exam tip

*Remember that transpiration is the evaporation of **water vapour** from the surfaces of the cells and its diffusion down a water potential gradient from a high water potential (usually inside the leaf) to a low water potential (usually outside the leaf).*

How science works

Growing food for humans to eat is now a big business which requires carefully controlled conditions. These are often provided in glasshouses which use technology to monitor and control environmental conditions such as temperature, carbon dioxide and water levels.

Minerals: what's needed?

Humans need minerals in their diet in order to grow properly. Plants do as well.

Humans get their minerals from their food. Plants get their minerals from the soil, dissolved in the water that enters the roots.

Plants photosynthesise to make sugars as their food. They need minerals to turn these sugars into proteins and DNA.

The following table shows some different minerals and how plants use them.

Element required	Main source	Used by plants to produce:
magnesium	magnesium compounds	chlorophyll for photosynthesis
nitrogen	nitrates	amino acids for making proteins which are needed for cell growth
phosphorus	phosphates	DNA and cell membranes to make new cells for respiration and growth
potassium	potassium compounds	compounds needed to help enzymes in photosynthesis and respiration

Deficiency diseases

Mineral **deficiencies** lead to poor plant growth. The next table shows the effect of mineral deficiencies on growth.

Mineral	Effect of deficiency on growth
magnesium	yellow leaves
nitrate	poor growth and yellow leaves
phosphate	poor root growth and discoloured leaves
potassium	poor flower and fruit growth and discoloured leaves

We can set up experiments to show that mineral deficiency leads to poor growth. The apparatus is shown in the following diagram.

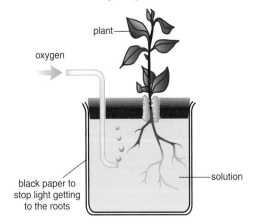

Several beakers of solution are used:

- One has all minerals the plant needs.
- Each of the others is deficient in one mineral.

Exam tip

You need to be able to explain this experiment if you are asked about it.

The plant with all the minerals will grow well. The plants with minerals missing will show the signs of deficiency detailed in the previous table.

Minerals are usually present in the soil in low concentrations. Their concentrations are higher in the roots than in the soil – so they cannot diffuse into the root hairs.

The plants must move these minerals against their concentration gradient instead, using **active transport**. This requires energy, which comes from respiration, so roots need lots of oxygen to respire.

Test yourself

1 How can you show that water is transported up the stem of a plant?

2 This diagram shows a potometer. It is a device for measuring the uptake of water by a leafy shoot.

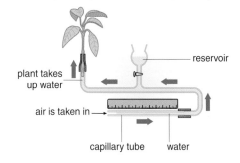

(a) After 20 minutes the water has moved along the capillary tube. Which way will it move? Explain your answer.

(b) The water moves 30 mm in 20 minutes. Calculate the speed of movement in millimetres per minute.

(c) If the apparatus was placed in windy conditions, would the water move faster or slower? Explain your answer.

3 What quantitative method would you use to show that water is lost from a plant, using the following apparatus: potted plant, digital scales, polythene?

4 How do some plants get help from other plants in obtaining their minerals?

5 Why do plants need to use energy to take up minerals from the soil?

B4e Energy flow

After revising this item you should:

- be able to explain pyramids of numbers and biomass, how the efficiency of energy transfer between organisms shapes them, and how we can transfer the energy in biomass.

Pyramids

All living organisms need energy. Ultimately this energy comes from the Sun.

This energy:

- is absorbed by plants and enters food chains
- flows through food webs and whole ecosystems
- is harnessed by humans, e.g. for agriculture.

The following diagram shows a simple food chain.

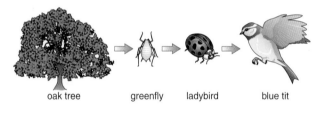

oak tree   greenfly   ladybird   blue tit

The producer is the first organism in every food chain. All the other organisms in the chain are consumers.

The food chain shows which organisms consume which other organisms, but it does not give us any information on how many organisms there are at each stage.

Instead we can draw a **pyramid of numbers**.

1   Count the number of organisms at each stage (**trophic level**) of the food chain.

2   Draw a box to scale to represent these numbers.

The pyramid of numbers does not take into account the size of each organism. For this we need to construct a **pyramid of biomass**. This shows the mass of living material at each stage of the food chain or food web.

The next diagram shows two pyramids.

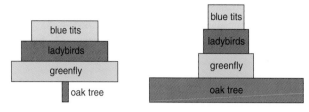

Pyramid of numbers.   Pyramid of biomass.

In the pyramid of numbers the oak tree is shown as a small box as it is only one tree. In the pyramid of biomass the oak tree is shown as a large box because it has a large mass of living material.

Energy in food chains

Energy from the Sun flows through food chains by:

- photosynthesis
- feeding

Photosynthesis produces glucose. When consumers eat plants the energy locked up in the glucose passes to the animal. The energy passes from consumer to consumer as each organism feeds.

Some of the energy is transferred to less useful forms of energy at each trophic level. This leaves the food chain by:

- heat from respiration
- **egestion** (waste material from a cell or organism).

The following diagram shows how energy moves through a food chain.

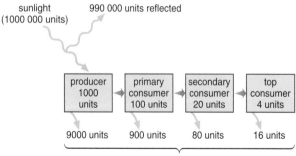

Look back at the pyramid of biomass at the top of the page. The efficiency of energy transfer explains its shape. The more energy is lost at any trophic level, the less energy there is to be passed to the next stage.

This loss of energy also explains why food chains rarely contain more than five or six organisms. There is not enough energy left at the end to support more levels.

Energy from biomass

Humans can harness and use the energy in plant **biomass** (the mass of living material) in different ways.

Here are some ways of transferring energy from biomass:

- burn wood from fast growing trees
- ferment biomass using yeast to produce alcohol
- ferment biomass using bacteria to produce biogas.

There are several reasons for developing these **biofuels**:

- Renewable – they do not run out.
- Reduce air pollution by carbon dioxide.
- Provide energy self-reliance to countries that do not have fossil fuel reserves.

Humans can choose to use biomass in many ways. They can:

- use it as fuel • eat it • feed it to animals
- grow it (seeds) to make more plants.

Test yourself

1 Construct a food chain containing five organisms.

2 Draw a pyramid of biomass for this food chain.

Organism	Mass (kg)
lettuce	100
slug	15
frog	5
adder	1

3 Look at the diagram of energy flow in a food chain (page 45).

   (a) How much energy is lost from the food chain in total?

   (b) Calculate the percentage of energy passed from the producer to the primary consumer.

   (c) Is this more or less energy than that passed from the primary to the secondary consumer?

4 Explain how energy is lost from a food chain and whether the lost energy can be used in any way.

B4f Farming

Intensive farming

Many farmers try to produce as much food as possible from the amount of land, plants and animals available. They use **intensive farming** methods to achieve this.

Intensive farming methods of food production improve the efficiency of energy transfer. They do this by reducing the energy transferred (or lost):

- to pests • to competing plants.

Intensive farming also reduces energy lost as heat as animals are kept in pens indoors. Our use of these methods can raise ethical dilemmas. They may be efficient and produce more food – but they also can lead to environmental problems.

For example, pesticides:

- can harm useful organisms, like plant-pollinating insects
- can enter the food chain – sometimes the pesticides do not break down and as they accumulate (build up) in animals higher up the food chain, they may kill them.

The next diagram shows how this happens.

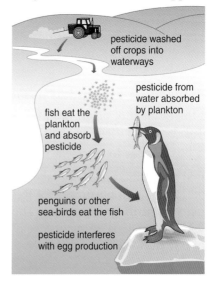

pesticide washed off crops into waterways

pesticide from water absorbed by plankton

fish eat the plankton and absorb pesticide

penguins or other sea-birds eat the fish

pesticide interferes with egg production

Soil-free farming

Plants are usually grown in soil, but not always. Growing plants without soil is becoming increasingly popular. The technique is known as **hydroponics**.

Crops are sometimes grown in artificial soil or in water. This is particularly useful for growing tomatoes in glasshouses or where the soil is very poor. The next table shows some of the advantages and disadvantages of hydroponics.

Advantages	Disadvantages
better control of mineral levels	lack of support for the plant
better control of disease	need to add fertilisers

Organic farming

Organic farming has become more widespread recently (although intensive farming techniques are still far more common). Organic farming is where no artificial fertilisers, pesticides or herbicides are added to the soil.

The table shows the function of each of these chemicals.

Chemical	Function
fertiliser	adds minerals to help plant growth
pesticides (including insecticides and fungicides)	kill pests: • insecticides kill insects • fungicides kill fungi
herbicides	kill plants (weeds)

Many different techniques are used in organic farming:

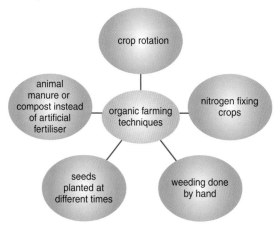

Organic farming has many benefits but it also has some disadvantages.

Advantages	Disadvantages
no artificial chemicals which can harm the environment	labour intensive – crops weeded by hand
possible health benefits of organic food to humans	organic food costs more in the shops
allows varied seed planting times and crop rotation to avoid diseases	

Biological control

Pesticides kill pests. Organic farming uses natural methods to control pests instead of artificial pesticides. Natural methods are those that use living organisms to control the pests. The organism is usually a predator that eats the pest.

The table shows some advantages and disadvantages of **biological control**.

Advantages	Disadvantages
the control organism only kills the pest	sometimes the control organism can become a pest itself
no artificial pesticides are needed	if the pest is wiped out, other organisms higher in the food chain may die through lack of food

We need to be careful when using biological control techniques. Removing a pest from a food chain or food web can cause problems for other organisms because their food source is removed.

Test yourself

1 Explain why battery farming of chickens is an example of intensive farming. How does battery farming reduce energy lost by the chickens?

2 How does crop rotation help organic farming?

3 Give an example of biological control.

4 Use this table to answer the questions.

Organism	What they eat	Molecules of insecticide in their body
aphid	plant sap containing ten molecules of insecticide	10
ladybird	100 aphids	
thrush	1000 ladybirds	
sparrowhawk	2000 thrushes	

(a) Calculate how much insecticide each organism contains and fill in the table.
(b) How much more insecticide is in the sparrowhawk's body compared with the aphid?
(c) Why does the insecticide harm the thrush but not the aphid?

B4g Decay & B4h Recycling

After revising these items you should:

- understand what decay is, what causes it and what affects its rate, explain how food is preserved, understand the carbon and nitrogen cycles and explain how bacteria contribute to the recycling of nitrogen.

Causes of decay

All organisms are made of organic material and when organisms die this breaks down. This is the process of **decay**.

If decay did not happen then all the dead organisms would remain. Decay releases the nutrients from their bodies and these can be recycled.

The following table shows how different conditions affect the rate of decay.

temperature	warmer conditions allow more decay because they favour the growth and reproduction of microorganisms that cause decay
amount of oxygen	microorganisms need oxygen to respire aerobically so the rate of decay is greater when oxygen is plentiful
amount of water	microorganisms need water to dissolve substances and to respire – if the conditions are too dry, there will be no decay

The ideal conditions for decay are the presence of warmth, oxygen and water. Without these, decay slows down.

Decomposers and detritivores

Two main groups of organisms bring about decay.

decomposers (e.g. bacteria and fungi)	• these organisms are **saprophytes** • they release enzymes onto the dead organisms then absorb the partially digested material • this is **saprophytic** feeding
detritivores (e.g. earthworms, maggots and woodlice)	• these organisms help the decomposers • they feed on the dead and decaying material (**detritus**) and break it down into smaller pieces with a larger surface area for decomposers to work on

Every autumn the leaves fall from the trees. Why have they disappeared by the following spring?

1 Detrivores eat the leaves and earthworms pull them into the soil. This starts the breakdown process.
2 Decomposers in the soil continue the breakdown.
3 Chemicals in the leaves are released into the soil and taken up by roots to be reused by plants the following year.

In some conditions, e.g. waterlogged soils with no oxygen, decay is restricted so the nutrients are not available to the plant roots.

Food preservation

All organic material decays but sometimes we want to delay this process. For example, fruit needs to be kept fresh and free from decay.

To prevent or reduce the rate of decay, various methods of **food preservation** can be used. The following table shows some preservation methods and how they prevent decay.

Preservation method	How decay is prevented
canning	the high temperature kills the microorganisms water and oxygen cannot get into the can after it is sealed
cooling	the low temperature slows down the growth and respiration of microorganisms
drying	microorganisms cannot respire or reproduce
freezing	microorganisms cannot respire or reproduce because their chemical reactions are slowed down
adding salt or sugar	the sugar or salt draws water out of the microorganisms
adding vinegar	the vinegar is too acidic for the microorganisms preventing their enzymes from working

How science works

Food preservation means that we can now transport food over large distances without it going off. For instance, fresh fruit and vegetables can be flown in from countries in Africa.

Some people are concerned about 'food miles' – how far the food has been transported to reach us – because this releases carbon dioxide which contributes to global warming.

But growing fruit and vegetables to export is an important source of income to poor people in developing countries, so making an ethical choice when buying food can be difficult.

Recycling

Recycling is nothing new. Bacteria and fungi have been recycling nutrients for millions of years. They decompose dead animals and plants, releasing the nutrients so that they are available for living plants and animals to take in.

If this did not take place living organisms would not have a supply of carbon and nitrogen. These two elements are the most commonly recycled and you need to know about the carbon and nitrogen cycles.

The carbon cycle

Carbon is the basic element that makes up the molecules that build organisms. It is found in carbohydrates, proteins and fats.

The main source of carbon is from the carbon dioxide in the air.

- This is incorporated into living organisms when plants photosynthesis.
- Carbon is trapped in carbon compounds, which are passed along food chains and food webs.
- Carbon returns to the air as carbon dioxide when animals and plants respire.
- Soil bacteria and fungi (decomposers) release carbon dioxide into the air during aerobic respiration.

The carbon cycle is shown in the next diagram.

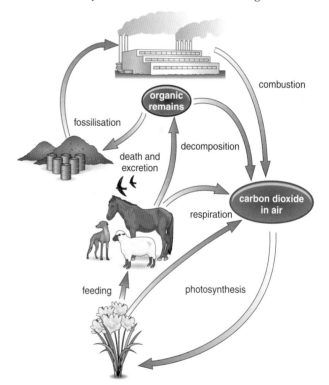

Another part of the carbon cycle is the making and burning of fossil fuels. Some organisms may not decay and become fossils instead. They are compressed underground and turn into fuels. Burning releases the carbon trapped in these fuels.

Carbon is also recycled in the sea:

1 Marine organisms make shells out of **carbonates**. Carbonates contain carbon.

2 The organisms die and their shells fall to the sea bed.

3 These are compressed and turn into limestone.

4 The limestone gets worn away by weathering or by volcanic activity.

5 Carbon dioxide is released into the air and joins the cycle again.

The nitrogen cycle

The air is made of 78 per cent nitrogen but it is too unreactive to be used by animals or plants.

Instead, plants take in nitrates from the soil to make protein for growth. These nitrogen compounds are passed along food chains and webs as organisms feed.

When animals and plants die, the compounds are broken down by decomposers back into nitrates and returned to the soil.

This is the nitrogen cycle.

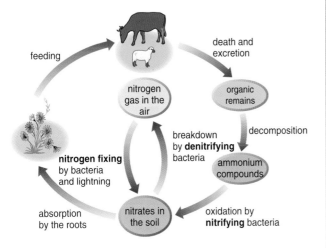

At each stage of the cycle specialised bacteria are responsible for the conversion of one nitrogen compound into another.

Type of bacteria	What they do
decomposing (live in the soil)	convert proteins from dead organisms and **urea** (waste material) into ammonia
nitrifying	convert this ammonia into nitrates
denitrifying	change nitrates back into nitrogen gas
nitrogen-fixing (live in the soil or in the root nodules of leguminous plants, e.g. clover)	remove nitrogen gas from the air (lightning also does this)

Test yourself

1 Fish can be preserved by freezing, drying and canning.

   (a) What do these methods have in common?
   (b) How are the three methods different?

2 A warden on a nature reserve notices that the egg shells of some birds are damaged by pesticides. But the reserve where the birds live is not polluted with pesticides. Explain why the birds' eggs are affected.

3 How do leguminous plants help to recycle nitrogen?

4 Making compost is encouraged by local councils. Waste material such as vegetable peelings, leaves and grass are ideal for the compost heap.

   (a) What living organisms need to be in the compost heap for decay to occur?
   (b) Sometimes water is added to compost. Explain why.
   (c) Why do gardeners usually turn their compost heaps?

5 Explain why respiration and photosynthesis are important in the carbon cycle.

B5a In good shape

Skeletons

Skeletons can be:

- inside the flesh (endoskeletons), or
- outside the flesh (exoskeletons).

Internal skeletons are an advantage over external skeletons.

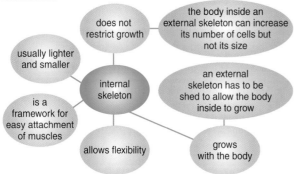

Bone and cartilage

Human skeletons are made of bone and **cartilage**. These are living tissues. Both are susceptible to infection but they can grow and repair themselves.

Bones start off as cartilage.

- The cartilage is slowly replaced by the addition of calcium and phosphorus (**ossification**).
- The growth spurt in adolescence is when the cartilage at the ends of long bones produces more bone.
- When most of the cartilage has been turned into bone, you stop growing. Doctors can tell if a person is still growing or not by the amount of cartilage that is there.

A long bone is a hollow structure consisting of:

- a head covered with cartilage
- a shaft containing bone marrow with lots of blood vessels.

The hollow structure of long bones makes them stronger than solid bones of the same mass.

Bone problems

Bones can be easily damaged. A sharp knock will break a bone.

A broken bone is called a fracture.

- Simple fractures involve only bone.
- Compound fractures involve other tissues as well, such as skin.

It is dangerous to move a person with a suspected fracture because the broken bones could pierce another organ or even sever the spinal cord. This could result in paralysis.

Osteoporosis is a disease suffered mainly by elderly people.

- It is caused by loss of minerals from the bone, through poor diet or lack of exercise.
- This makes the bone soft.
- As a result elderly people are more susceptible to fractures if they fall.

Joints

Synovial joints are movable and allow different degrees of movement.

The following table shows types of movable joint.

Type of synovial joint	Where it's found	Degree of movement
ball and socket	shoulder hip	rotational
hinge	elbow knee	movement in one plane

This diagram shows a synovial joint. The table below shows parts of the joint and their functions.

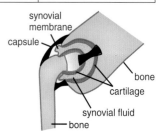

Part of synovial joint	Function
synovial fluid	lubricates the moving surfaces reduces friction
synovial membrane	secretes synovial fluid keeps fluid within the joint
cartilage	reduces friction
ligaments	attach bone to bone and keep the joint together

Artificial joints

There are many joint diseases, which mean pain and restricted movement for the sufferer. But we can replace hip and knee joints with artificial joints.

There are advantages and disadvantages for patients deciding whether or not to have this medical procedure.

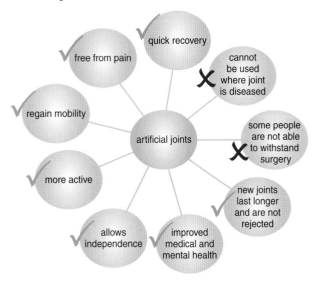

Muscles

Muscles pull a bone to move it when they contract.

- Muscles can move bones only when they are contracting.
- When muscles are not contracting they are relaxing.

One muscle will move a bone in one direction – it needs another muscle to move it back again. So muscles work in pairs. The pair of muscles are called **antagonistic muscles**.

An example of this is the muscles involved in bending (flexing) and straightening your arm.

Bend arm	Straighten arm
biceps contracts	**triceps** contracts
triceps relaxes	biceps relaxes

Your arm is an example of a lever. The elbow joint is the pivot of the lever.

The following diagram shows how the biceps and triceps work antagonistically.

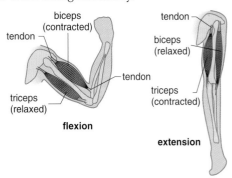

flexion

extension

1 Explain why the skeleton of a human makes a person more flexible than a lobster.

2 John and his grandmother were involved in a car accident. Explain why John had no broken bones but his grandmother broke several bones.

3 Where in an adult body will you find cartilage?

4 Explain how the early signs of osteoporosis can be detected.

5 Explain what causes osteoporosis.

B5b The vital pump & B5c Running repairs

After revising these items you should:

- be able to explain how the heart works, understand its role in the circulatory system and understand the problems that can arise and how they can be treated.

Circulation

Our understanding of the circulatory systems is largely down to the work of two men.

- Galen (c130–200 AD) thought that blood was made in the liver and flowed from the heart to the organs and back again, like the tide.
- Harvey (1578–1657) suggested something very different and described the circulation as we know it today. He predicted the existence of capillaries between arteries and veins, although he did not have a microscope powerful enough to see them.

A circulatory system is made up of:

• a heart   • blood vessels   • blood.

There are two types of circulatory system – single and double.

Fish have a **single circulatory system**. The blood goes through a two-chambered heart once in a full circuit.

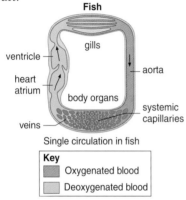

Single circulation in fish

Key
Oxygenated blood
Deoxygenated blood

Humans have a **double circulatory system**. Their blood has two circuits.

• In one circuit, deoxygenated blood is pumped from the heart to the lungs and oxygenated blood returns to the heart.

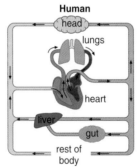

Double circulation in humans

• In the second circuit, oxygenated blood is pumped to the body and deoxygenated blood returns to the heart.

To achieve this double circulation, humans have a four-chambered heart. The oxygenated and deoxygenated blood is kept completely separate.

The heart

The heart is a double pump with four chambers – two atria and two ventricles. Both sides of the heart pump together.

The following table shows the blood vessels associated with the heart.

Blood vessel	Type of blood	Transports blood from:	Transports blood to:
vena cava	deoxygenated	body	right atrium
pulmonary artery	deoxygenated	right ventricle	lungs
pulmonary vein	oxygenated	lungs	left atrium
aorta	oxygenated	left ventricle	body

The blood inside the heart flows from the atria to the ventricles. There are valves between the atria and ventricles to prevent backflow into the atria.

The passage of blood flow through the heart is the **cardiac cycle**.

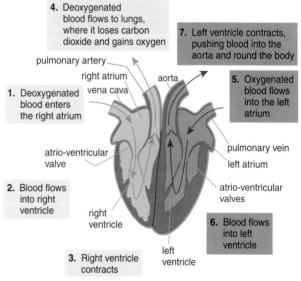

The cardiac cycle is shown on an electrocardiograph (**ECG**). See page 54 for an example of an ECG.

Heart and activity rate

The volume of blood flowing through different organs varies. It also changes when you exercise.

The table on page 54 shows the blood flow through different organs at rest and during exercise.

	Blood flow (cm³/min)	
Structure	At rest	During exercise
brain	700	740
heart	200	750
kidneys	1000	600
liver	1400	600
lungs	100	200
skeletal muscles	750	12000
skin	300	1900

Exam tip

You should be able to interpret data on blood volume and relate it to different parts of the body.

- More blood flows to those parts of the body used during exercise, such as skeletal muscles, so they can release more energy.
- Less blood flows to those organs not used in the exercise, such as the liver.

Heart rate is linked to activity. The more active you are, the higher your heart rate.

- Muscles used during exercise need more oxygen, so the heart pumps more blood to them.
- Hormones such as **adrenaline** also increase heart rate.

Heart muscle contraction is controlled by groups of cells called the **pacemaker**. These cells complete a small electric circuit.

The pacemaker produces nerve impulses.

- Impulses in the **SAN** (sino-atrial node) make the right and left atria contract together.
- Impulses in the **AVN** (atrio-ventricular node) make the two ventricles contract.

An ECG shows nerve impulses detected by electrodes attached to the chest wall.

This is an ECG trace for a normal person.

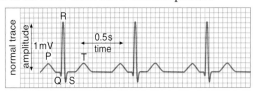

Key
P impulse causing atria to contract
QRS impulse causing ventricles to contract
T recovery before next heart beat

Doctors can use an ECG to see if a patient's heart is normal or not.

- Tachycardia is shown by the QRS waves being different heights and closer together.
- In heart attack patients the T wave is often upside down.

Artificial pacemakers can now be fitted in patients with heart problems to control the heartbeat.

Another way of showing heart rate is by using an **echocardiogram**. This bounces ultrasound waves off the heart. It produces moving pictures of the beating heart.

Heart problems

The heart and circulatory system can go wrong. Some causes are shown below.

Lifestyle:
- Diet – too much fat (blocks arteries) and salt (increases blood pressure)
- **Alcohol** – increases blood pressure
- Smoking – increases blood pressure
- Stress – increases blood pressure
- Drugs – increase blood pressure

Heart conditions and diseases:
- **Hole in the heart** – blood passes directly from the right atrium to the left atrium, bypassing the lungs. This can be corrected by surgery.
- Damaged or weak valves – valves can fail or you can be born with a faulty valve. In both cases the problem valve can be replaced with an artificial one.
- Coronary heart disease (CHD) and heart attacks – CHD is when fat deposits in the coronary arteries reduce the blood flow to the heart muscle. This starves the cells of oxygen and they die (a heart attack). **Bypass surgery** can be used to replace a blocked artery.

Surgeons can replace severely damaged hearts. This involves a **heart transplant**.

- The damaged heart is removed and replaced by a healthy donor heart.
- There are heart **assist devices** which do the job of a diseased heart until a donor can be found.

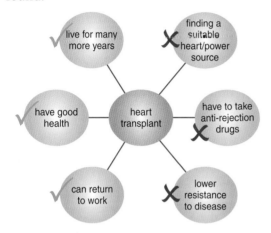

Blood

Parts of the blood have different functions:

Part of blood	Function	How structure is related to function
red blood cells	carry oxygen to the cells	contains haemoglobin which combines with oxygen in the lungs and releases it in the tissues shape – a biconcave disc increases surface area for taking up oxygen
white blood cells	kills foreign **bacteria** helps with immunity	some white cells engulf bacteria some white cells produce antibodies
platelets	help with blood clotting	release chemicals which make the **blood plasma** sticky
plasma	carries substances around the body	substances are dissolved in the plasma

Blood donors

Blood is needed during operations. **Blood donors** are people who donate their blood. Donated blood:

- is tested for blood group so it can be given to a person with the same blood group
- can also be used in **blood transfusions**.

The following table shows the blood groups and the antigens and antibodies associated with each.

Blood group	Antigens on red blood cells	Antibodies in the blood serum
A	A	anti b
B	B	anti a
AB	A and B	nil (neither anti b not anti a)
O	nil (neither A nor B)	both (anti b and anti a)

Antibodies and antigens are called **agglutinins** and are found in blood.

If a person is given blood of the wrong type, clumps of cells form. This is called agglutination.

Blood clotting

Blood normally clots at the site of cuts. Sometimes it clots inside blood vessels. Anticoagulant drugs can be used to stop blood from clotting.

Haemophilia is an inherited condition in which blood does not clot easily.

Substances that affect blood clotting	Drugs used to control blood clotting
- vitamin K - alcohol - green vegetables - cranberries	- **warfarin** - **heparin** - **aspirin**

1 Look at the table showing blood flow to different organs (page 54).

(a) Calculate the increase in blood flow to the heart in cubic centimetres per minute (cm^3/min).

(b) Explain why there is an increase.

2 Why are the walls of the left ventricle thicker than the walls of the right ventricle?

3 These ECG traces show abnormal hearts.

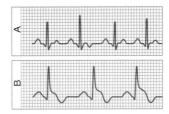

For each trace:

(a) Describe the differences from a normal heart.

(b) Suggest what the heart problem is.

4 Explain why a person with a hole in the heart feels tired and lacks energy.

5 The table shows deaths from coronary heart disease (CHD) in 2004.

	Age		
	Under 35	35–64	65 and above
men	136	11260	47159
women	36	2812	44439
total	172	14072	91598

(a) Calculate the total number of deaths in 2004 from CHD.

(b) Are men or women more at risk from CHD? Explain your answer.

(c) Suggest reasons why fewer men under 35 die from CHD than those aged over 35.

B5d Breath of life

- be able to explain gaseous exchange in animals and humans and describe the symptoms of different respiratory diseases and the treatment of asthma.

Gaseous exchange

All living things need oxygen for respiration to release energy from food. The methods of obtaining oxygen are different in different animals and this can restrict where they live.

- Fish have **gills** to extract oxygen from water so they have to live in water.
- Amphibians have gills in the early stages of life but adults have developed lungs so that they can live on land.

These diagrams show how a fish exchanges gases with its surroundings (water).

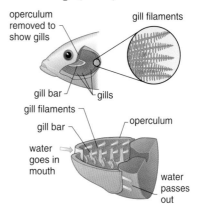

For efficient gaseous exchange the gills have:

- gill rakers to filter out particles that could damage them
- gill bars that support the gill filaments
- gill filaments which allow oxygen to diffuse into the blood and carbon dioxide to diffuse out of the blood.

Lungs and gaseous exchange

The structure of the respiratory system means efficient diffusion of oxygen and carbon dioxide.

The lungs do this by having:

- a large surface area of alveoli • moist surfaces
- thin membranes • a good blood supply.

Breathing involves many parts of the respiratory system. It is made up of:

- breathing in (inspiration)
- breathing out (expiration).

The following table shows what happens to parts of the system.

Part	Breathing in	Breathing out
intercostal muscles	contract	relax
diaphragm	moves down	moves up
ribs	move upwards and outwards	move downwards and inwards
volume of chest cavity	increases	decreases
pressure	decreases	increases
air movement	sucked in	pushed out

A **spirometer** trace shows what happens to the volume of air intake and output during normal and deep breathing.

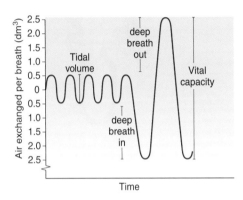

- When you breathe out as much air as you can, some air is still left in your lungs. This is the **residual air**.
- **Tidal air** (volume per breath) is the air entering and leaving your lungs at rest.
- **Vital capacity** is the maximum volume of air you can take in and breathe out in one large breath.

Respiratory system and disease

The lungs are a 'dead end' and so are prone to diseases. The respiratory system has ways of protecting itself from disease.

In the bronchi and trachea:
- production of mucus traps particles entering the system
- ciliated cells have cilia which move the mucus out of the system.

This spider diagram shows some lung diseases and their causes.

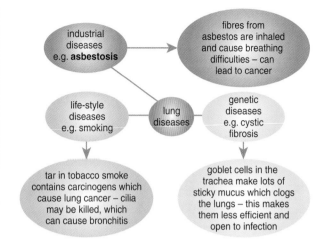

Asthma

Asthma is a condition caused by a narrowing of the tiny air passages in the lungs.

Allergens that trigger asthma attack	Symptoms	Treatment
• animal fur • feathers • pollen • dust mites • cigarette smoke • fungal spores • perfumes • pesticides	• tightness in the chest • coughing • difficulty breathing	• inhalers to relax the muscles around the airways • drugs to inhibit the allergic reactions

Peak flow is a measurement of how much air is getting into and out of the lungs. These diagrams show what happens during an asthma attack.

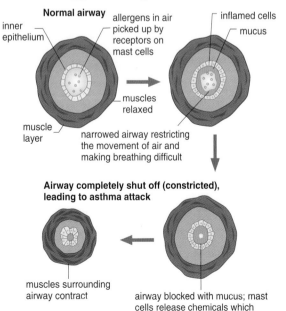

1 What is gaseous exchange?

2 What features do the gaseous exchange surfaces of fish and humans have in common?

3 Using the spirometer trace (page 57) calculate:

   (a) the tidal volume   (b)   the vital capacity
   (c) the extra air taken in during a deep breath
   (d) the residual air.

4 Explain how the trachea and bronchi are kept free from dust and bacteria.

5 Why are the lungs a 'dead end?'

6 The table shows deaths from some respiratory diseases.

Disease	Number of deaths		
	Women	Men	Total
lung cancer	11 000	32 000	43 000
bronchitis	4000	11 500	15 500

   (a) Calculate the total number of deaths from these two diseases.
   (b) Suggest why more men die from lung cancer than women.
   (c) What is a possible cause of lung cancer?

B5e Waste disposal

● be able to explain the structure of the kidneys and how they work and understand how the body cools itself.

Kidneys

The **kidneys** are part of the excretory system. They excrete urea, excess water and salt.

● The **liver** produces urea during the breakdown of excess **amino acids**.

● Excretion is getting rid of the waste products of metabolism (chemical reactions in the body).

This diagram shows the structure inside a kidney and the blood vessels that serve it.

The kidney contains tiny nephrons, where blood is filtered and where useful and waste products are separated.

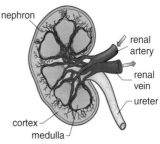

This diagram shows details of a nephron and what happens at three stages along its length.

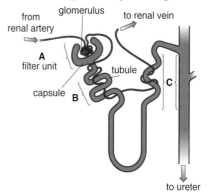

● A – Small molecules are filtered out of the blood into the capsule, under pressure, to form the filtrate.

● B – **Selective reabsorption** – glucose and amino acids are removed from the filtrate and passed back into the blood.

● C – Some salt and water are reabsorbed to keep their levels in the body balanced.

Urine

The following table shows the factors that affect **urine** production.

Factor	Effect on urine production
high temperature	more
low temperature	less
more exercise	less
less exercise	more
increased water intake	more
decreased water intake	less

The concentration of urine is controlled by the anti-diuretic hormone (ADH) produced by the **pituitary gland** in the brain.

When your body is dehydrated, **ADH** is produced to make your kidneys reabsorb more water. The next diagram shows the way it works.

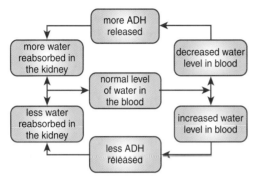

The ADH mechanism is a **negative feedback** mechanism. This is a control mechanism where a rise in the level of one substance brings about a reduction in the level of another:

- A rise in ADH brings about a reduction in water in the urine.
- A fall in ADH results in more dilute urine.

Dialysis

A **dialysis** machine is used for people with kidney failure. It removes urea and maintains the levels of sodium and glucose in the blood.

The following diagram shows a dialysis machine connected to a person with kidney failure.

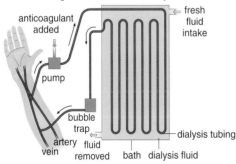

- Blood is removed from the arm and passed through selectively permeable dialysis tubing in the machine.
- As the blood passes through, it is bathed in dialysis fluid which has a similar composition to normal plasma.
- Urea and excess water and salt diffuse out of the tubing into the fluid.
- Glucose does not diffuse out as there is an equal or higher concentration of glucose in the fluid.

Carbon dioxide

Respiration produces carbon dioxide, which increases carbon dioxide levels in the blood. The brain detects this increase.

These high levels of carbon dioxide must be removed from the body. A control centre in the brain increases the rate and depth of breathing to get rid of it.

Sweating

Sometimes the body temperature increases. This could be after exercise or during an illness.

Sweating occurs to keep the body temperature at 37°C. Extra heat energy is used to evaporate sweat.

If your body temperature is higher than this heat energy is transferred from the body to water molecules, which escape from the skin as sweat.

This loss of heat energy means that the skin (and body) cools down.

Test yourself

1 Urea is a poisonous substance.
   (a) Where is it produced?
   (b) Why is it produced?
   (c) Which organ gets rid of urea?

2 Explain how the structure of the kidney enables it to produce urine.

3 Explain how the concentration of urine is controlled by ADH produced by the pituitary gland.

4 Look at the diagram of a dialysis machine (opposite).
   (a) Why is an anticoagulant added?
   (b) Why is a bubble trap included?
   (c) Why does glucose stay in the blood?

5 After playing a football match, players sweat more, breathe faster and breathe more deeply. Explain why.

B5f Life goes on

After revising this item you should:

- be able to explain how and why hormones control the stages of the menstrual cycle, describe fetal investigations and explain treatments for infertility.

The menstrual cycle

Women produce eggs between puberty and menopause. During these years there is a repeating cycle every 28 days – the **menstrual cycle**.

The next diagram shows the main stages of the menstrual cycle.

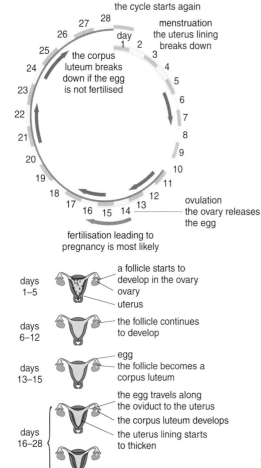

The next table shows the four hormones that control the menstrual cycle.

Hormone	Function
oestrogen	thickens the uterus in preparation for a fertilised egg
	stops the pituitary gland making **FSH**
progesterone	produced by the corpus luteum maintains the uterus wall
	(fall in progesterone triggers menstruation)
follicle stimulating hormone (FSH)	stimulates the production of follicles in the ovary
luteinising hormone (**LH**)	makes the follicle (after release of the egg) develop into the corpus luteum

The following diagram shows how these hormones interact.

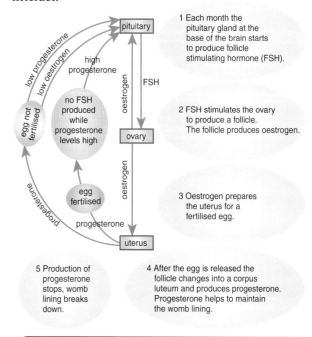

1 Each month the pituitary gland at the base of the brain starts to produce follicle stimulating hormone (FSH).

2 FSH stimulates the ovary to produce a follicle. The follicle produces oestrogen.

3 Oestrogen prepares the uterus for a fertilised egg.

4 After the egg is released the follicle changes into a corpus luteum and produces progesterone. Progesterone helps to maintain the womb lining.

5 Production of progesterone stops, womb lining breaks down.

> ### Exam tip
>
> *You must learn the series of events in the menstrual cycle and how they are controlled. Use the table and the diagram above to help you.*

Infertility

Sometimes fertilisation does not happen naturally. This is called **infertility**.

The following table shows some of the treatments to help those who are infertile.

Treatment	How it works
artificial insemination	sperm is inserted into the female artificially
using follicle stimulating hormone (FSH)	this is given to females who fail to ovulate, to promote ovulation
in vitro fertilisation (**IVF**)	• eggs are removed from the female and fertilised in a glass dish by doctors • the fertilised eggs are then put back into the female's uterus
egg donation	eggs are taken from a donor, fertilised by IVF and put in the female's uterus
surrogacy	the fertilised egg is placed in the uterus of another female to carry the fetus and give birth
ovary transplants	a woman can receive a healthy ovary from a donor

There are arguments for and against these treatments.

Treatment	Argument for	Argument against
artificial insemin-ation	if the man cannot make sperm, donated sperm can be used	some people do not want donated sperm
FSH	enables the woman to get pregnant	sometimes many eggs are released, which can produce multiple births
in vitro fertilisation	good for females with blocked oviducts	some people see it as unnatural
egg donation	for females who do not produce their own eggs	some women do not want donated eggs
surrogacy	the natural mother cannot have a normal pregnancy	some people see it as unnatural
ovary transplants	if the ovary is damaged or diseased	some people see it as unnatural

How science works

Technology has allowed doctors to help females who cannot get pregnant to have babies. There are risks to mother and baby as a result of some procedures.

Think about the ethical and economic issues that need to be considered.

Fetal investigations

Fetal screening is used to monitor a pregnancy. Ultrasound scans produce images of the fetus. The scans:

- can detect the sex
- can determine the number of fetuses
- can detect some abnormalities
- do not harm the fetus or the mother.

Other investigations involve removing cells from the fluid surrounding the fetus.

- Chromosomes from the cells are tested to find out if the fetus has any abnormalities.
- This procedure is called **amniocentesis**.
- It can be used to identify **Down's syndrome** and other genetic disorders.

There is a risk of early miscarriage as a result of the amniocentesis.

These investigations raise ethical issues, such as:

- What should parents do if an abnormality is discovered: continue with the pregnancy or consider terminating it?

Test yourself

1 Explain why a female has a period each month.

2 Using the information in the table of hormones (page 60), construct a flow diagram to show the sequence of events in the menstrual cycle.

3 Explain the options open to a couple who cannot have a baby naturally.

4 Explain why a female might not have an amniocentesis.

5 As a result of fetal screening, a fetus is shown to have Down's syndrome. What ethical issues does this raise?

B5g New for old & B5h Size matters

After revising these items you should:

- be able to explain the problems and ethical issues surrounding organ donation, explain how patterns of human growth are affected by internal and external factors and know how we can monitor this.

Donor organs and transplants

When organs inside the body malfunction, they can be replaced with donor organs.

There are problems in the supply of donor organs because they:

- are in short supply
- must be a tissue match to the recipient
- must match the size and the age of the recipient.

Also there are ethical issues concerning organ donation.

- Who should receive the donor organ?
- Donor organs must be collected and transplanted as soon as possible. This means distance has to be considered.
- Religious and cultural views have to be considered. The recipient may have views on the religious or cultural origin of the person who donated the organ. Some blood and tissue types are more commonly found in some cultures rather than others.

If the transplanted organ is not a good blood and tissue match, the recipient's body may **reject** the new organ.

1   The organ may have the wrong antigens on its cells.
2   This triggers an attack by the recipient's white blood cells.
3   The white cells called T cells begin the rejection process.
4   The blood vessels in the rejected organ start to deteriorate and then cells die.
5   Eventually the organ dies.

A drug called Cyclosporine was developed which stops the white blood cells from rejecting the transplant. Drugs of this sort are **immuno-suppressive drugs**.

> **Exam tip**
>
> *You should be able to describe the steps leading to rejection of a transplanted organ.*

Mechanical replacements

Some organs can be replaced with mechanical or electronic devices instead of a donor organ.

This can lead to problems:

- The device must be small enough to fit inside the body. This is being overcome with advances in micro engineering.
- A reliable power source must be found for the device, which can be recharged from outside the body.
- The material used to make theses devices must be strong, non-toxic, lightweight and non-corrosive.
- They must not cause allergic reactions in the body.

The following table shows two groups of mechanical replacements.

Those used outside the body	Those used inside the body
• **iron lung** • **heart and lung machines** • dialysis machines • hearing aids	• joints • heart pacemakers • heart valves • eye lenses • hearing aids

Organ donors

Donors can be living or dead.

A living, healthy person can donate an organ such as a kidney.

- The donor must be a close match in blood and tissue type.
- This is more likely if the donor is a relative because they are more likely to have some genes that are the same.
- Living people cannot donate if they only have one of the organ concerned, such as a heart.

Healthy organs can be used from a donor who has just died.

- The donor must have a close match in blood and tissue type.
- They must be of a similar age and size.

The Anthony Nolan Trust keeps a list of people who are willing to donate their bone marrow to those who need it.

There are suggestions that a national register of donors should be kept. Others suggest that people should have to opt out of such schemes rather than volunteering to join them.

The bar chart shows the number of lung transplants at a US hospital.

You can see that the number of transplants is increasing each year. Another way of showing data is a graph of how long patients survive after transplant surgery.

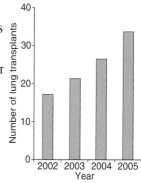

Height and growth

All humans start life as a fertilised egg. This divides by mitosis to produce identical cells.

The identical cells start to differentiate and become specialised. As the cells increase in number the person grows.

Some people grow taller than others. Extremes in height can occur and the known extremes of human height are 57–272 cm.

Height is controlled by genes and hormones.

The pituitary gland in the brain produces a **growth hormone**, which stimulates growth in the long bones.

- **Giantism** is caused by an overactive pituitary gland.
- **Dwarfism** is caused by an underactive gland.

Other hormones that affect growth are:

• the sex hormones   • insulin.

Growth can be affected by diet.

• Fit and well-fed youngsters will grow to their full potential.
• Those who lack some part of their diet may have their growth restricted or become obese.

Exercise plays an important part in ensuring that people grow and develop normally.

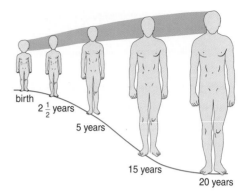

birth
2 ½ years
5 years
15 years
20 years

Monitoring growth

Growth charts are used as a guide to compare individuals.

This chart shows typical height curves for girls aged 2- to 18-years-old.

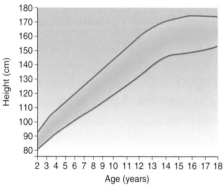

The normal range is in the centre, between the red lines. If the height is outside this area, the girl may have a growth problem due to hormonal or developmental problems.

How science works

Data is collected from developing children and analysed to produce charts which show normal ranges of growth.

These charts can then be used to indicate those children whose growth is outside the normal range.

The length, mass and head size of babies are regularly measured during the first months of life. We can plot these measurements on **average growth charts** to highlight any growth problems.

Different parts of the body grow at different rates. It is important to compare the proportions of different parts.

The following diagram shows how the relative proportions change.

Life expectancy

People are living longer. Some of the possible reasons are:

• fewer industrial diseases   • healthier diet
• better life style   • modern treatments
• more cures for diseases   • better housing.

The following table shows some of the problems this can cause on a personal and national level.

Personal	National
help needed to live in their own home	increasingly ageing population
might have to sell homes to afford to live in a residential home	more money needs to be spent on pensions, hospitals and social care
cannot get upstairs easily	more burden on the tax payers

Test yourself

1 After a kidney transplant, the organ was rejected. Explain why this happened and what could have be done to avoid rejection.

2 Look at the lung transplants bar chart (page 62).
   (a) How many lung transplants were there in 2003?
   (b) How many more transplants were there in 2005 than in 2002?

3 Suggest advantages and disadvantages of a national register of organ donors.

4 Look at the typical height curve for girls (opposite).
   (a) What is the normal range of heights for a ten year old?
   (b) A six year old is 90 cm tall. What does this suggest about her growth?

5 Using the human growth chart above, describe what happens to the size of the head when compared with the overall height.

B6a Understanding bacteria

Shape and structure

Bacteria come in a variety of shapes:

• spherical • rod • spiral • curved rods.

They all have the same basic structure. The next diagram shows this structure and the following table shows the functions of the parts.

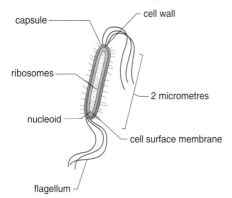

Structure	Function
capsule	a sticky coat that stops the bacterium from drying out – not all bacteria have a capsule
ribosomes	small spherical structures that build protein from amino acids
nucleoid	contains most of the bacterial DNA – unlike a nucleus, it does not have a membrane around it
flagellum	enables the bacterium to swim
cell wall	a rigid protective wall that gives the cell its shape and stops it from bursting
cell surface membrane	controls which substances can enter and leave

Bacterial cells are very different to animal and plant cells.

They do not contain:

• a proper nucleus • mitochondria
• chloroplasts • a vacuole.

Some bacteria consume organic nutrients (chemicals) while others can make their own (a form of photosynthesis).

This means that bacteria can:

• survive on an enormous range of energy sources
• exploit a wide range of habitats.

Reproduction

Bacteria reproduce by a type of asexual reproduction called **binary fission**. The cells split in two.

One bacterium in ideal conditions can split into two every 20 minutes. Because bacteria reproduce so rapidly:

• they can be grown in large tanks called **fermenters**
• food contaminated with bacteria can spoil very quickly
• bacterial diseases can cause symptoms very quickly.

Yogurt making

Bacteria are used in food manufacture. The production of yogurt, vinegar and cheese all involve bacteria.

The main stages in yogurt making are:

1 **Sterilisation** of the equipment using bleach or steam.
2 **Pasteurisation** of milk – heating it to 72°C for 15 seconds and then cooling it rapidly. This kills any active bacteria in the raw milk.
3 Addition of bacterial **culture** (*Lactobacillus*) and incubation at 46°C. This turns the milk sour by changing the lactose in the milk into lactic acid.
4 Sampling to check the correct bacteria are still present.
5 Addition of flavours and colours, then packaging.

It is important that everyone handling bacteria do so safely, so that no harmful bacteria contaminate the culture or affect those working to produce it.

Test yourself

1 State the function of each of these bacterial cell parts.

   (a) flagellum
   (b) cell wall
   (c) DNA.

2 Explain why bacteria are so successful.

3 Draw a table to show how bacterial cells differ from plant and animal cells.

4 What are the consequences of the rapid reproduction of bacterial cells?

5 Describe and explain the stages in the production of yogurt.

B6b Harmful microorganisms & B6c Microorganisms – factories for the future?

After revising these items you should:

● understand how bacteria cause disease, describe the work of scientists involved in tackling diseases, explain how yeast is used in brewing and understand how distillation can increase the alcohol content.

Pathogens and disease

A pathogen is an organism that causes disease.

Pathogens include:

• some bacteria

• viruses

• **protozoa**.

The following table shows the organisms that cause some diseases and how they are spread.

Disease	Cause	How it is spread
food poisoning	*Salmonella, E. coli* (rod-shaped bacteria)	eating raw or undercooked food contaminated with faeces poor personal hygiene
cholera	*Vibrio* (comma-shaped bacteria)	drinking water contaminated with faeces
dysentery	*Entamoeba* (single-celled protozoan)	drinking water contaminated with faeces
influenza	influenza (RNA) virus (various types)	tiny drops of mucus and saliva containing the virus are spread either by coughs and sneezes or by touch
septicemia	*Staphylococcus* (spherical bacteria)	infected puncture wounds, animal bites or by sharing hypodermic needles

Some pathogens are spread easily in the air and in untreated water.

Stages of an infectious disease

Any infectious disease goes through several stages.

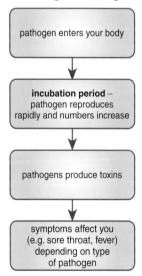

pathogen enters your body

incubation period – pathogen reproduces rapidly and numbers increase

pathogens produce toxins

symptoms affect you (e.g. sore throat, fever) depending on type of pathogen

Natural disasters

Earthquakes and flooding can cause loss of life and damage to property. Survivors are at risk from diseases such as cholera, dysentery and food poisoning.

The rapid spread of disease is caused by:

- disruption to water and sewage supplies
- breakdown of the electricity supply so there is no refrigeration and food decays quickly
- damaged roads and transport systems so health workers cannot get to the people to treat them.

Scientists and the treatment of disease

Three scientists in particular carried out pioneering work on diseases.

Pasteur and the **germ theory of disease**
- Pasteur showed that microorganisms turned wine into vinegar.
- By heating the wine you could kill the microorganisms that caused this.
- He showed that if microorganisms were passed for one organism (in silkworms) to another then so was the disease.

Lister and the development of antiseptics
- Lister introduced carbolic acid disinfectant during operations to prevent infection.
- Chemicals were also used to kill microorganisms on instruments and skin.

Fleming and the discovery of penicillin
- Fleming noticed that a mould (*Penicillium*) killed other bacteria.
- Later Florey and Chain succeeded in extracting the antibiotic penicillin from the mould.

How science works

Pasteur, Lister and Fleming all had ideas which they struggled to investigate. Over time they managed to test their theories and slowly their ideas were accepted.

Antibiotics and antiseptics

Antibiotics and **antiseptics** are used to control disease.

Antibiotics are drugs which:

- can be swallowed or injected into the body
- kill or slow down the growth of bacterial colonies
- do not harm the person.

Antiseptics are chemicals which are used:

- outside the body
- to kill bacteria on the skin
- to kill bacteria on surfaces and instruments.

Yeast and fermentation

Fermentation is the breakdown of sugars by **yeast** in the absence of oxygen. The yeast carries out anaerobic respiration.

$$\text{glucose} \rightarrow \text{ethanol (alcohol)} + \text{carbon dioxide}$$
$$C_6H_{12}O_6 \rightarrow 2C_2H_5OH + 2CO_2$$

Exam tip

You must learn these word and symbol equations. Remember:

- *no oxygen gas is involved*
- *only C, H and O atoms are present.*

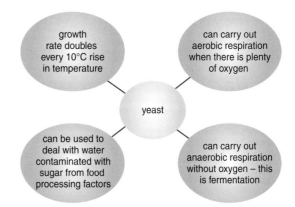

growth rate doubles every 10°C rise in temperature

can carry out aerobic respiration when there is plenty of oxygen

yeast

can be used to deal with water contaminated with sugar from food processing factors

can carry out anaerobic respiration without oxygen – this is fermentation

Yeast can reproduce rapidly. Its optimum growth rate is controlled by:

- availability of food
- temperature
- pH
- removal of waste products.

The following graph shows how much alcohol beer contains when brewed at different temperatures. The more alcohol there is, the more sugar has been broken down.

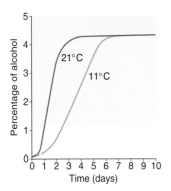

Brewing at lower temperatures saves energy but takes longer.

Beer and wine production

The following diagram shows some of the main stages of beer and wine production.

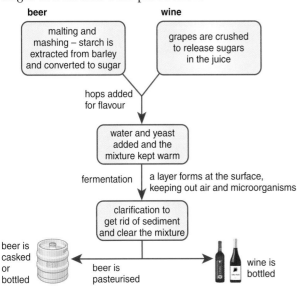

- The layer that forms over the fermenting mixture is carbon dioxide.
- As the alcohol concentration in the mixture rises, it kills off yeast cells so fermentation eventually stops.
- Pasteurisation kills off any remaining yeast once fermentation is finished.
- Pasteurisation is needed otherwise fermentation could continue, causing casks or bottles to burst, which would be dangerous.

Distillation

Different strains of yeast can tolerate different levels of alcohol. So there is a natural limit to the alcohol content of a fermented mixture.

To produce spirits, which have a very high alcohol content, you need to carry out **distillation**.

Examples of spirits are:

- rum from cane sugar
- whisky from malted barley
- vodka from potatoes.

The pure alcohol is separated from fermented sugar by boiling it and condensing the vapour.

Beer and wine can be made at home but, by law, distillation must be carried out commercially on licensed premises.

Test yourself

1 A person is suffering from a sore throat.

    (a)   What is the probable cause?
    (b)   Describe how the microorganism caused the sore throat.

2 A tsunami hit a developing country. Many survivors later died. Explain why.

3 What are the differences and similarities between an antibiotic and an antiseptic?

4 Look at the graph of temperature and alcohol production.

    (a)   How long does it take to get to the maximum percentage of alcohol at 21°C?
    (b)   Give one reason for and one against fermenting at 11°C.
    (c)   Why does fermentation not produce high levels of alcohol? How could you achieve this?

B6d Biofuels

After revising this item you should:

- be able to explain how biogas is produced and used and explain how biofuels affect the environment.

Biogas

Bacteria break down organic material and produce **biogas**. Different organic material needs different bacteria to break it down.

Biogas is a mixture of gases containing:

- mainly **methane**
- some carbon dioxide
- traces of hydrogen, nitrogen and hydrogen sulfide.

Biogas containing more than 50 per cent methane burns easily. Biogas containing about 10 per cent methane is explosive.

Biogas is produced from animal dung, rotting vegetable peelings and compost.

- Anaerobic bacteria turn the organic material into methanol, hydrogen and a mixture of formic and ethanoic acid.
- Different bacteria change these compounds into methane and carbon dioxide. This is biogas.
- For efficient production oxygen must be excluded and the temperature maintained at 15°C.

Biogas as a fuel

Biogas can be:

- burned to generate electricity
- burned to produce hot water and steam for central heating systems
- used as a fuel for buses.

It is a cleaner fuel than diesel and petrol but does not contain as much energy as natural gas.

Commercial production of biogas

The next diagram shows a simple digester that could be used to make biogas using the continuous flow method.

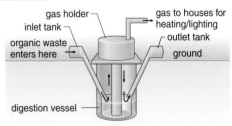

- Organic material such as human and animal waste is regularly tipped into the digester.
- The digester is below ground level to help maintain an even temperature. If the temperature falls the bacteria will not be active and the production of biogas decreases.
- At high temperatures enzymes are denatured and the bacteria die. The optimum temperature is about 40°C.
- Gas collects in a gas holder at the top of the digester.
- The sludge at the bottom is harmless and can be used as fertiliser.

The use of digesters in remote areas such as in China has meant that villages can have electricity made from waste.

This technological advance gives villagers a better lifestyle. Having electricity improves their social and economic conditions.

Advantages of biofuels

There are many advantages of using biofuels to generate electricity and run vehicles.

Biofuel	Fossils fuel
✓ once burned, more can be grown, so they will not run out – they are a sustainable resource	✗ take millions of years to be made, so will eventually run ozut
✓ return the same amount of carbon dioxide to the air as they took out when growing	✗ add carbon dioxide to the atmosphere when burned – this is a greenhouse gas, and adds to global warming
✓ methane is a greenhouse gas, but overall biofuels are cleaner	✗ produce other polluting gases and particulates as well as carbon dioxide
✓ do not produce particulates, so are less harmful to health	✗ particulates in the air cause health problems, such as breathing difficulties

Test yourself

1 Explain how methane is produced using the continuous flow method.

2 Look at this bar chart.

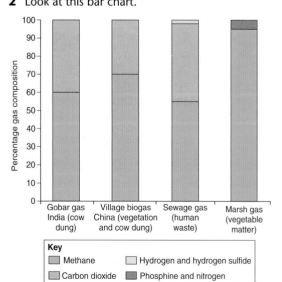

(a) Name four gases found in biogas.
(b) Which gas has the highest percentage in all types of biogas?
(c) Which type of gas comes from human waste?

3 Why are different types of bacteria needed to break down organic material?

4 Explain the advantage of using biofuels instead of fossil fuels in relation to:

(a) sustainability
(b) the effects on greenhouse gases.

5 Give a disadvantage of using biofuels on a large scale.

B6e Life in soil & B6f Microscopic life in water

After revising these items you should:

- understand the feeding relationships of organisms living in the soil, and their role in nutrient cycles and soil fertility, understand that plankton form the basis of many food webs and know the effects of water pollution on organisms.

Food webs

We can link together organisms in the soil in food chains and food webs.

Food chains show that one living organism eats another. Food chains link to form food webs.

A typical food web contains:

- **herbivores** (e.g. slugs, snails, wireworms), which eat plant material
- detritivores (e.g. earthworms, millipedes, springtails), which feed on dead organic matter
- **carnivores** (e.g. centipedes, spiders, ground beetles), which feed on other animals.

The following diagram shows a soil food web.

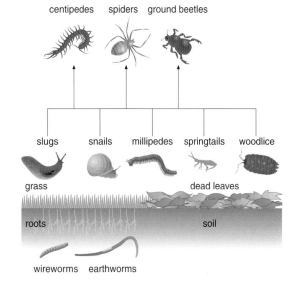

- There are fewer carnivores than herbivores or detritivores because each carnivore needs many food organisms to stay alive.
- Energy is lost as it goes from one level to the next.
- More detritivores will be found in the dead leaves as they feed on dead organic matter.
- More herbivores will be found on the living grass.

Soil

- Most soil organisms and plants must have a supply of oxygen and water to survive. Oxygen is needed for respiration.
- Water is needed for plant roots to take up minerals and for chemical reactions.

Most organisms do not like acidic soils. Lime can be added to neutralise the acidity.

Soil can be made more fertile by mixing, so the humus and dead matter on the top is mixed with the lower layers. This speeds up the process of decay by microorganisms.

Earthworms

Earthworms are very important to soil structure and fertility. They:

- bury organic matter for decomposition by bacteria and fungi
- aerate and drain the soil
- mix up the soil layers
- help to neutralise the acid soil.

If you jump up and down on the soil, earthworms will come to the surface. Charles Darwin noticed this. He studied earthworms in a wormery and noticed that they drag leaves and other organic matter down into their burrows.

He realised the importance of earthworms in improving the structure and fertility of the soil. They eat the leaves and leave their waste on the surface or in the soil. This helps to mix the soil.

> **How science works**
>
> To understand why the earthworm is important, Darwin collected data from his observations of the wormery and analysed his findings. He used this to develop theories.

The nitrogen cycle

It is important that elements such as nitrogen, carbon, sulfur and phosphorus are recycled.

- Carbon is the basis of all organic molecules.
- Sulfur and phosphorus are used to make proteins.
- Nitrogen is essential for plant protein. Although nitrogen makes up 80 per cent of the Earth's atmosphere, most plants are unable to use this directly. They absorb nitrates from the soil.

The next diagram shows the nitrogen cycle and the parts played by different bacteria.

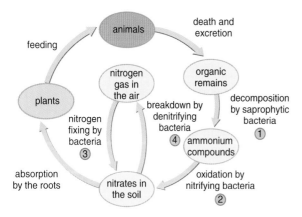

There are four types of bacteria in the nitrogen cycle:

1 Saphrophytic soil bacteria which start the decomposition – turn dead organic remains into ammonia.

2 Nitrifying bacteria (e.g. *Nitrosomonas* and *Nitrobacter*) – turn ammonia into nitrates.

3 Nitrogen fixing bacteria (e.g. *Azotobacter, Clostridium* and *Rhizobium*) – turn gaseous nitrogen into nitrates.

4 Denitrifying bacteria (e.g. *Pseudomonas*) – turn nitrates back into nitrogen gas.

Denitrifying bacteria are found mainly in waterlogged soils and they remove nitrates. Aerating a waterlogged soil decreases the activity of these bacteria.

Living in water

A wide variety of organisms live in water. The following diagram shows the advantages of this:

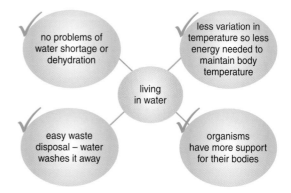

The main disadvantage of living in water is regulating water content within the body.

Organisms have to maintain the correct water balance within their bodies. If the body fluid is more concentrated than the surroundings:

- water will enter by osmosis, and
- the body will swell up.

This extra water must be removed.

The opposite happens if the surroundings are more concentrated than the body fluid.

- Many single celled organisms such as amoebae pump surplus water entering the cell into a **contractile vacuole**.
- This empties when it is full.

Salmon have a double problem because they move from fresh water to salt water and back again. The body has to adjust to each new environment.

- When salmon are at sea they lose water by osmosis and produce very little urine.
- When they enter fresh water they produce lots of dilute urine.
- They also try to prevent water entering their bodies by secreting mucus.

Another disadvantage of living in water is resistance to movement. Many aquatic organisms have a streamlined shape so that movement through the water is easier.

Some organisms such as frogs and insects spend part of their lifecycle on land and part in water. They get the benefit of both habitats.

Plankton

Plankton are microscopic organisms that live in water.

- **Phytoplankton** are microscopic plants that are capable of carrying out photosynthesis.
- Zooplankton are microscopic animals.

The size of the plankton population depends on:

- light
- temperature
- availability of nutrients.

These factors change with the seasons, and this changes the number of plankton in an area.

Seasonal changes cause **algal blooms**. These are rapid increases in the amount of plankton brought about by increased light and temperature or nutrients circulated during storms. The next graph shows this seasonal increase.

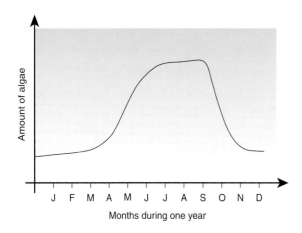

Water pollution

Water in streams and rivers can become polluted with pesticides and fertilisers that run off farmland. Sewage also pollutes waterways. This causes **eutrophication**.

Eutrophication is the end point of this series of events as shown in the following diagram.

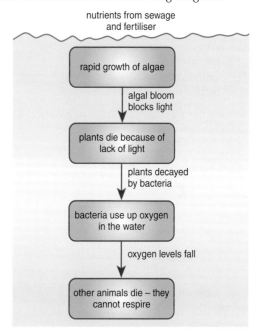

Some artificial chemicals accumulate in the bodies of marine organisms, such as PCBs (used in electrical equipment) and DDT (an insecticide, banned in the 1970s).

1 The chemicals enter the water system.
2 Plankton absorb the chemicals and they are passed up the food chain.
3 They become concentrated in the fat and are not broken down.
   - The highest concentrations are found in the top carnivores.
   - The chemicals can cause cancer, liver damage and even death.

Indicator species

Some species of organisms are used as biological indicators for pH and oxygen levels. Their numbers in samples of river water tell scientists how clean or polluted the river is.

- Mayfly and stonefly larvae only live in very clean water.
- Freshwater shrimps and water lice tolerate some pollution.
- Bloodworms and rat-tailed maggots like to live in polluted water.

Test yourself

1 Why are few animals and plants found in waterlogged soils?

2 (a) Explain why detritivores are important in a food web.
   (b) Why are earthworms called natures ploughmen?
   (c) Explain why farmers do not want denitrifying bacteria in their soil.

3 Salmon can live in both salt and fresh water. Why would this be a problem for other fish such as trout?

4 Explain how the amoeba controls the amount of water in its body.

B6g Enzymes in action

After revising this item you should:

- understand how and why we use enzymes in washing powders and in the food industry and explain the advantages of using immobilised enzymes.

Biological washing powders

Enzymes are biological catalysts. They have many uses both inside and outside the human body.

The following table shows the enzymes in biological washing powders.

Type of enzymes	Type of stain	Products formed
lipase	fats and oils	fatty acids and glycerol
protease	proteins	amino acids
amylase	carbohydrates, e.g. starch	simple sugars (usually glucose)

The products formed are soluble and will wash out of clothes easily.

Biological washing powders work best at low temperatures and at neutral pH.

- Enzymes have an optimum pH and temperature at which they work most efficiently.
- If the water is the wrong pH (too acidic or too alkaline) they will not work as effectively. This is because pH affects the shape of an enzyme.
- Enzymes are proteins. High temperatures alter their shape – they are denatured.

Making sugar sweeter

The sugar we buy in the shops is **sucrose**. This can be broken down into two simpler sugars by the enzyme **sucrase** (**invertase**).

The reaction is shown by the equation:

$$\text{sucrose} + \text{water} \xrightarrow{} \text{glucose} + \text{fructose}$$
$$C_{12}H_{22}O_{11} + H_2O \xrightarrow{\text{sucrase}} C_6H_{12}O_6 + C_6H_{12}O_6$$

Glucose and **fructose** are both much sweeter that sucrose when you taste them.

The food industry makes use of this property.

- Foods can be sweetened by adding glucose or fructose rather than sucrose.
- This means less sugar is needed.

Immobilising enzymes

Enzymes are expensive to industry because they have to be extracted from living tissues and purified. So the food industry does not want to 'lose' the enzymes it uses. The enzymes are immobilised.

This can be done in different ways:

- Attach the enzymes to plastic beads or a sheet of material. This allows them to be removed from the mixture when the reaction is complete.
- Surround the enzymes by a permeable jelly called alginate (which is made from seaweed).

Immobilising enzymes has these advantages:

- The product is not contaminated with the enzymes.
- Enzymes in **alginate beads** can be used in continuous flow processing. In this process the liquid to be treated flows over the beads in a reaction vessel and produces a continuous supply of the product. This is much more convenient than treating separate batches of liquid.

Lactose free

Lactose (milk sugar) is found in cow's milk. Some people and all cats are intolerant of lactose.

- The lactose cannot be digested and passes into the large intestine where it is fermented by bacteria.
- This produces a lot of gas.
- The undigested lactose also interferes with the reabsorption of water by the colon, causing diarrhoea.

Lactose-free milk is made by adding the enzyme lactase.

- The enzyme is first immobilised in alginate beads.
- The milk is passed over the beads and lactase converts lactose into glucose and **galactose**.
- Both of these sugars can be absorbed by people and cats, without side effects.

Test yourself

1 Rory works with machinery and his clothes get covered in grease. What sort of washing powder should he use to get his clothes clean? Explain why.

2 Anne found that the stains in her trousers were not removed when she washed them in a biological washing powder. Suggest reasons for this.

3 How does the food industry make sweet, low calorie foods?

4 Explain why immobilised enzymes are used in the food industry.

5 Freda takes her cat to the vets because it is suffering from diarrhoea. What could the vet suggest to overcome this problem?

B6h Genetic engineering

After revising this item you should:

- understand the main steps used in genetic engineering and be able to explain how insulin can be synthesised and how crops can be improved.

Altering the code

Genetic engineering alters the genetic code of an organism by inserting genes.

The organism that contains these inserted genes is called a **transgenic** organism.

The following diagram shows how transgenic cells are produced.

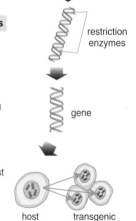

Extraction of DNA
- cells containing the required gene are broken up to release their DNA
- the DNA extract is mixed with enzymes called restriction enzymes

Cutting the DNA with enzymes
- the restriction enzymes act like scissors and cut the DNA into shorter lengths

Isolating the gene
- the section of DNA containing the gene is now isolated ready to put into the host cell

Inserting the gene
- the genes are put into the host cells. This can be done in several ways
- some of the cells take up the genes. When they divide the genes are copied so that all the daughter cells have been transformed

Replicating the gene
- large numbers of cells can be cultivated

Special groups of enzymes cut the DNA.

- **Restriction enzymes** cut DNA into short lengths. They look for specific sequences of DNA. Different restriction enzymes cut the DNA in different places.
- **Ligase** enzymes are used to rejoin DNA strands.

Once the new gene has been inserted into the cut DNA of the transgenic organism, it is important to check that the new gene has been transferred correctly and that it works.

An **assaying technique** is used to do this.

- The new gene is attached to a marker gene that produces bioluminescence (glows in the dark).
- Not all genes splice correctly but those that do will glow in the dark in the new organism.

Producing human insulin

Bacteria can be used in genetic engineering to produce human insulin.

The process is shown in the diagram.

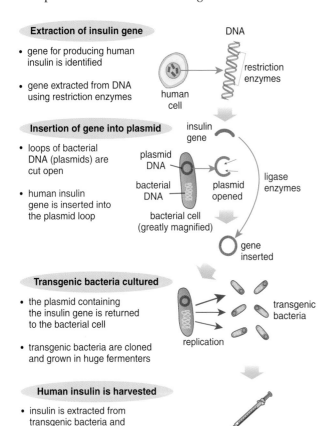

Extraction of insulin gene
- gene for producing human insulin is identified
- gene extracted from DNA using restriction enzymes

DNA
human cell
restriction enzymes

Insertion of gene into plasmid
- loops of bacterial DNA (plasmids) are cut open
- human insulin gene is inserted into the plasmid loop

insulin gene
plasmid DNA
bacterial DNA
plasmid opened
ligase enzymes
bacterial cell (greatly magnified)
gene inserted

Transgenic bacteria cultured
- the plasmid containing the insulin gene is returned to the bacterial cell
- transgenic bacteria are cloned and grown in huge fermenters

replication
transgenic bacteria

Human insulin is harvested
- insulin is extracted from transgenic bacteria and purified for use by diabetics

Diabetics use insulin to control their blood sugar level.

Improving crops

Genetic engineering can improve crops:

- Increase the yield by making the crops grow bigger/faster.
- Make crops resistant to disease and weed killers. A field can be sprayed with weed killer, which kills the weeds but does not damage the crop.
- Make plants produce chemical such as vitamins. In Asia the diet of rice is lacking in vitamin A so genetically engineered rice containing a gene to produce vitamin A has been produced. Now by eating this rice the diet is not deficient in vitamin A.
- Help plants survive in poor conditions such as drought or salty water.

Advantages of genetic engineering	Disadvantages of genetic engineering
✓ produces crops which can resist drought, need less fertiliser, make their own pesticides and produce greater yields ✓ can make chemicals, e.g. insulin without killing animals ✓ can help humans who have diets deficient in certain trace elements ✓ faster than selective breeding	✗ unexpected allergic responses when the food is eaten ✗ pest resistance may spread to wild plants ✗ lasting environmental damage ✗ human health may be affected

How science works

Genetic engineering has benefits and risks.
- It alters plants so that traditional farming methods of pest control are no longer needed.
- This affects the social and economic environment of developing countries.

Test yourself

1 What is genetic engineering?

2 List the main stages of genetic engineering.

3 How is bioluminescence being used in genetic engineering?

4 Why are some people worried about genetic engineering?

5 Explain how a scientist could genetically engineer a wheat crop so that it produces more wheat seeds.

Exam-style questions

1 Cystic fibrosis is caused by a recessive allele, carried by about one person in 20. Only a person with two recessive alleles has the disorder. The recessive allele is represented by **f**.

(a) What is the probability of two carriers having a child that has the disorder?

....[1]

(b) What is the probability of two carriers having a child that is a carrier?

....[1]

(c) What is the genotype of someone with the disorder?

....[1]

(d) What is the genotype of a carrier?

....[1]

(e) Some diseases are caused by mutations. Mutation can be caused by many different things. Write down three of these things.

....
....
....[3]

2 Plants live in all parts of the world.

(a) Explain **two** ways in which a plant is adapted to live in hot dry places.

....
....[2]

(b) A plant has colourful petals. How is it pollinated?

....[1]

(c) Give an advantage of a plant having small, light pollen.

....[1]

(d) Plants make their own food by photosynthesis. Write down the products of photosynthesis and state how they are used by the plant.

....
....
....[3]

3 (a) Use examples to explain the difference between unicellular and m]ulticellular organisms.

....
....[2]

(b) Explain the advantages of being multicellular.

....
....
....[3]

(c) Complete the diagrams by writing the number of chromosomes in the circles. [2]

(d) During growth, cells and organisms enlarge in size. How is plant cell growth different to animal cell growth?

....
....
....[3]

4 (a) In a glasshouse the tomato plant leaves start turning yellow.

(i) Which two mineral elements are missing?

....
....[2]

(ii) How could the grower make the leaves green again?

....[1]

(b) There are more minerals in the root of a plant than in the soil, yet minerals are taken up from the soil. Explain how this can occur.

....

....[2]

(c) When the tomatoes have been harvested, the grower wants to recycle the nutrients still in the green parts of the plant. Suggest how she could do this.

....[1]

(d) The tomatoes are sold and some go to the canning factory. Explain how canning the tomatoes preserves them for longer than keeping them in a refrigerator.

....

....

....[3]

5 The table shows the number of deaths in one year from smoking-related diseases.

Disease	Number of deaths		
	Men	Women	Total
lung cancer	30000	10000	40000
heart attack	103000	77000	180000
bronchitis and emphysema	12000	4500	16500

(a) Draw a bar chart to show the deaths from lung cancer and bronchitis and emphysema for men and women. [3]

(b) Describe the symptoms of lung cancer.

....

....[2]

(c) How do the intercostal muscles and diaphragm cause changes in volume and pressure during inspiration?

....

....

....[3]

(d) List **four** ways in which the respiratory system ensures efficient gaseous exchange.

....

....

....

....[4]

6 (a) Which organism causes food poisoning?

....[1]

(b) How is cholera transmitted?

....[1]

(c) Why is the influenza virus called a pathogen?

....[1]

(d) Antibiotics and antiseptics are used to control disease. What is the difference between them?

....

....[2]

(e) After an earthquake diseases spread rapidly. Explain why.

....

....

....[3]

Answers to exam-style questions

1 (a) 1 in 4 / 25%   [1]

(b) 1 in 2 / 50%   [1]

(c) ff   [1]

(d) Ff   [1]

(e) Any **three** from: UV light / Chemicals in the environment / Chemicals in cigarette smoke / Background radiation   [3]

2 (a) Any **two** from: Long roots to reach water / Green stem for photosynthesis / Leaves reduced to spines to prevent water loss / Thick cuticle to prevent water loss / Reduced surface area to volume ratio to reduce water loss   [2]

(b) By insects   [1]

(c) The pollen can be blown easily by the wind   [1]

(d) Glucose and oxygen; Glucose and oxygen are used in respiration; Glucose is stored as starch / changed into cellulose for cell walls   [3]

3 (a) Amoeba is a unicellular organism made of one cell; Humans are multicellular organisms which means made of many cells   [2]

(b) Any **three** from: Allows the organism to be larger; Allows for cell differentiation; Allows the organism to be more complex; A single cell has a smaller surface area to volume ratio, reducing movement of materials in and out   [3]

(c) Mitosis – all 46; Meiosis – all 23   [2]

(d) Plant cell division is restricted to shoot and root tips; Plant cells retain the ability to differentiate; Cell enlargement is the main method plants use to increase in height   [3]

4 (a) (i) Nitrate; Magnesium   [2]

(ii) Add fertiliser   [1]

(b) By active uptake; Which uses energy   [2]

(c) Make compost with them   [1]

(d) Any **three** from: Canning kills bacteria in or on the tomatoes; Bacteria decays food; Canning stops more bacteria from entering; Refrigerator is cold and slows down bacterial growth but does not stop it   [3]

5 (a) Labelled axes: 'Number of deaths' on vertical axis, 'Disease' on horizontal axis; Number of deaths starts at '0' and ends at '30 000'; Bar graph displays data for men and women correctly   [3]

(b) Any **two** from: Shortness of breath / Blockage of airway / Lump in airway / Coughing   [2]

(c) Intercostal muscles contract, pulling ribs upwards; Diaphragm contracts / moves downwards; Volume increases and pressure decreases   [3]

(d) Any **four** from: Good blood supply / Thin membranes / Moist membranes / Large surface area / Secretion of mucus / Cilia   [4]

6 (a) *Salmonella* / *E. coli*   [1]

(b) In drinking water contaminated with faeces   [1]

(c) Influenza virus is an organism that causes disease   [1]

(d) Antibiotics kill bacteria inside the body; Antiseptics kill bacteria on the surface of the body   [2]

(e) Any **three** from: Damage to water supplies / Contamination of water supplies / Loss of power to appliances used for refrigeration / Food cannot be cooked properly / Food cannot be stored properly / Health services disrupted   [3]

Index of key words